'NUFF SAID

Tales of a South London Villain

CHARLIE BREAKER

ISBN: 9781641534345

www.charliebreaker.com

Contents

Introduction

I have written a collection of some of the more bizarre times in my life. Some are very different, some are totally crazy, some sexy, some very violent. Some serious crimes, murders, and underworld control stories.

You might know me, you might have been there or just heard the tales first or second hand. Some are South London stories passed down through the generations, from the old timers that were there.

On the run from the police several times took me to Newcastle, Hereford, Cornwall, Ireland and Tenerife where I was finally locked up. There were many drug and alcohol induced wild scenes at these venues.

I worked in Jamaica for many years, selling stolen car parts through my franchises. I was earning more in a day than most Jamaicans could in six months. This bought on a brilliant lifestyle that few could comprehend.

Back in Brixton, I opened the first ever white man run Reggae club, The Red Stripe. I then got seriously involved in the ganja trading world. I ended up as Mr Brixton, the top weed supplier to the Jamaican community. I was only two down the line from the famous smuggler, Mr Nice. Howard Marks became a long time friend, always on my doorstep but I never knew him then. He cast me in the film 'Mr Nice' and mentioned me a couple a times in the sequel 'Señor Nice'.

Charlie Bronson put me in his film 'Bronson' and

wrote about me in his books, as did media 'gangster', Dave Courtney. I played his uncle, Sir Charlie, in his blockbuster 'Hell to Pay'.

Check Mr Breaker in Lock Stock an' Two Smokin' Barrels.

No love stories here, only sex. No heroes, only villains. No justified nice guys, bad boys only.

My life was a whirlwind of crime, violence and sex, fuelled by drugs, booze and rock 'n' roll. Not the suitable for the weak hearted.

These jackanories are laced with rhyming slang, South London humour and culture.

If there's any decency about you at all, you won't read this book!

Tenerife

I had been to Tenerife many times, in fact I lived there for a while.

The first time I went to Tenerife, I didn't even know that it was an island. I thought it was mainland Spain. The visit wasn't really a holiday, it was a job and one that paid well.

I was sat in a friend's office on his motor front, putting the world to rights, when these two big villains walked in.

"Hey Ton, can we 'ave a little dicky bird in ya shell like, private like."

"It's OK Bob, this is Charlie, he's as good as gold and a close friend."

The two villains eyed me up and down, then continued.

"Well, we got some pie & mash that needs to go to Tenerife, it pays well."

"What's the plan boys?" said Tony.

"We'll have a small suitcase to be carried from Gatwick airport to Tenerife."

Tony looked across at me, knowing that I was up for anything that paid well.

"Well Charlie boy?"

"Well, Bob is it? What do you want me to do and what does it pay?"

Now the second face joined in. "We're far too well known to do it, so we will pay all expenses and five hundred on delivery and another five hundred back here on return."

"To do what exactly?"

"To take a small suitcase off us at Gatwick Airport and return it to us when your picked up from the airport in Tenerife."

"When you want it done?" I said.

"Get your passport here to Tony and he will let you know."

"I haven't got a passport." I admitted.

"Well you best get one fast." said the second face.

They wasted no more time, they both shook Tony's hand first, then turned to me and shook mine. They then disappeared into the new Jaguar outside waiting for them.

"You've jus' met the 'Two Bobs', good people to work wiv but don't mess wiv them!"

"No way, thanks for the intro Ton, not every day you get a bit a work to earn a bag a sand!"

"Charlie, you can get a yearly temporary passport in the post office now, they do it on the spot, all you need is a passport photo and knowing dodger Dave who works there. Give him any name you want, jus' buy him a beer next time you see him in the boozer."

"I'll go there now, how much are they?"

"It won't break the bank, it's £12.50."

"That's 'andy to know Ton."

I got my dodgy passport and handed it to Tony, who I saw most days, so when the day arrived, the Bobs collected my passport and returned with a ticket to Santa Cruz in Tenerife. It was only a few days away and the two Bobs said they would drop me off at the airport but not to make any contact with them until they arrived at Santa Cruz.

When the day arrived, they all met at Tony's car

front.

"Look Charlie boy, after we drop you off at the airport, even though we're on the same plane, you do not even look at us, let alone talk to us. This is very important and you jus' keep this little suitcase in your german band until we are outside the airport, understand?"

"Yer I got it."

The two Bobs nodded at me and Tony, there was no more to be said.

Santa Cruz was one of the old airports where there was no customs as such, you walked down the gangplank and out into the car park. Hunky-dory!

There was a nice car there waiting for me and the case. I exchanged the little case for £500. It seemed unreal. A monkey was a lot in the UK but here in Tenerife was a fortune. There was two hundred pesetas to the pound and in a cheap bar you could buy a 330ml bottle of San Miguel for 20 pesetas, that's ten bottles to the pound! Life was good!

They had booked me into an apartment in Los Cristianos for 5 days but I missed my flight, I was 'avin' it large! I'd met an old Brixton friend out here, on the trot from the Old Bill and we were 'avin' it!

Eventually I made it back, and there was a monkey waiting for me in Tony's office.

Good days!

It was the '80s

After an altercation with another geezer in an illegal drinker in Loughborough Junction, Brixton, one day I ended up on the street fighting with him. A decent straight right had put the man down outside the front door. Unfortunately he landed with his barnet on the granite kerb. With claret coming out of his shell-likes and his mince pies shut, and as he appeared not to be breathing, I feared the worst. Next day I was on a plane to Tenerife, from which in those days there were no extradition orders. On arrival I soon met my old pal Muscles, Dennis. Brixton Bwoy!

Muscles was out there for a similar reason and had not just opened Spartacus Gym, but recently also a night club on the main strip in Playa de las Américas. This was a new town that had popped up outside Los Cristianos since I was last there.

Muscles soon found a place for me to stay and I ended up working in Spartacus Gym. This suited me, as I had always worked out at the local gyms to keep trim.

After the gym, me and some of the other lumps that worked in the gym, would go down to Muscles' night club, Veronica's, and help him look after the place. This massive club was named after Muscles' wife and it was heaving with English tourists, a lot quite elephant's trunk. It was fast becoming famous as the only English run club.

The club had most of the trade in the area during the summer months and the locals were starting to notice.

One night, there was five of the body builders supporting Muscles in the task of controlling the drunk crowd of Brits in there. There was no steroids in those days, so these were mostly tough South London geezers who had built up there bodies the hard way. Most were wanted back in the UK by the Old Bill.

Early this night, much the shock of them all, about ten or twelve Spaniards had appeared in the doorway armed with baseball bats and pick axe handles. Before they had done any real damage, they were disarmed and thrown back down the many steps they had just ascended. By the time they had landed, most were bleeding, one way or another.

Pleased with their work, the chaps were having a laugh about it with a refreshing bevy at the bar, ready for the night's task of controlling a club full of drunken tourists. The Spanish were obviously pissed off with Veronica's getting the lion's share of the Brits' wonga.

As we were polishing off our bevies, in burst dozens of Guardia Civil. The boys and I realised we were beat and put our hands up to save any further problems, and were frogmarched down the steps to a fleet of cars.

Back at the local nick we were all charged with assault on the Spanish. We were Brits and had beat up a load of locals, we knew that no way was it worth discussing it with the Guardia. We were locked up in the newly built Playa de la Américas Guardia barracks.

The following Monday we were all up in court and sentenced to six years a piece. The majority of us had dodged a bit of porridge in the UK, now we had to face a sentence of paella in Spain.

The only prison in Tenerife in those days was at Santa Cruz, the industrial port city in the north. It was a shithole of Arab standards.

On arrival we were ushered into a massive smelly room full of sweating locals. There was no air conditioning or any way of cooling down on this hot Tenerife day, incarcerated in this sealed sweat pit. The lumps that we were, we commandeered six spaces together against the wall.

Every prisoner had a three inch thick bag of dried pampas grass as a bed and a space of about two feet between them. So this was to be our new home for the next six years. We were starting to think that we would be better off doing a bit of porridge in Wormwood Scrubs.

In this big room with probably about fifty men and boys, the toilet was a hole in the floor for all to watch us do our ablutions. We then had to then wipe our bottles with our germans. Then to wash them, we had to walk the whole length of the room to the other end, where there was a standpipe. This rusty brown liquid was also the supply of drinking water. You couldn't make it up!

I had heard about drug smugglers being locked up in Arab jails but had never thought that I would ever be in one similar myself.

When the food came round, it was rice swimming in gravy, it looked appalling. We decided to go without.

That night we watched in amazement as many inmates with trainers were tying them to their ankles by their laces, so no one could steal them whilst they slept. After, in the pitch dark, we could hear boys screaming, obviously being raped. I thought this place must resemble what the Devil had in mind for him on his demise. Perhaps Diablo couldn't wait.

The first visitor arrived on the second day, it was Veronica. Muscles told her the situation and, bless her, she went drove back the whole length of the island to the America's just to get six buckets of Kentucky Fried Chicken, from the only KFC on the island. We were hank marvin by then!

Then, slowly we got more and more visitors to lighten the task of Veronica. There were plenty of fast food outlets opening up on the South Coast by now and the geezers were more than happy to get any alternative to rice in gravy.

The second morning there, I was collected by a kanga and frogmarched to the Governor's office.

"Would you like a coffee?" The governor said in perfect English.

"Yes please Sir". The old prison ways soon fall into place.

"Black or white?"

"White please Sir"

"Sergio!" He shouted loudly.

The door opened and in walked a big Spaniard, in fact unusually big for a Spanish man.

"¿Sí Señor?"

"Dos cafés. Uno con leche y uno solo."

"Sí Señor."

The big man walked out the door and reappeared minutes later with the two coffees. He placed them on the Governor's desk. Not a word was spoken.

Then the Governor broke the awkward silence.

"Would you like some brandy in yours?" The man said, reaching deep down into his desk and pulling up a litre bottle of Fundador.

"Yes please Sir." I'd seen the fishermen in Los Cristianos do this when I first came to the Island in the '70s and always followed suit.

We both sipped at our coffees, I was getting increasingly more curious about what I was doing there.

"You may be wondering why you are in my office drinking coffee."

"Very much so!" I replied.

"You do realise that you don't have be here for six years, don't you?"

"How long then Sir?"

"Well it depends on how much you are prepared to pay and that goes for the other five as well."

"Obviously we would like to get out of here as soon as possible, how much did you have in mind?"

"I had about two million pesetas a head in my mind."

The 'about' meant that, like most things in Spain, it was negotiable. Two million pesetas was roughly ten grand. In the early '80s that was an awful lot of money, even to the load of villains that were locked up here.

"We couldn't afford to pay that amount Sir!"

"Well go back to your friends and discuss it."

I finished off my coffee, cooled down by the generous amount of strong Spanish brandy. Once again Sergio was called and I was frogmarched back to the sweat pit to join my friends.

Back in the big room, I sat down with my muckers and gave them the news. They were excited, to say the least. When he said the asking price their faces changed.

"How much?" They all shouted out in harmony.

Most of them had been on the island awhile and resources were running a bit low with a couple of them.

"Hey, we're in Spain, everything is negotiable!" I said.

"We need to get in touch with the families for help, I'm sure they wouldn't want you banged up in here for years!"

Muscles, Alby and I had a few bob available but the price still needed negotiating.

The coffee mornings with the Governor continued until I got it down to 500,000 pesetas, which was about

£2500. Now back to my friends.

After much discussion it was decided to settle for that amount. So I, not wasting time, soon found a kanga to take me to the Governor's office and the deal was settled.

"How soon can we be free?"

"As soon as the *dineros* are in my hand."

Well what could I say? The deal was done and the geezer needed paying.

Back in the sweat pit, there was much conversation, as the young men discussed how they was going to pay. It only took a few days for me and Muscles to arrange payment, but for the rest it seemed forever. Finally, after about a little over three weeks since we had been there, the rest had paid. Veronica was holding the folding matter. She bought it in and delivered it to the Governor.

Once again I returned to the office.

"OK Boss, we're all paid up now. When are we free?"

"Within a few days."

Well about three days later, they were all called for and handcuffed.

"Why the cuffs?" I Said.

"Only till you're on the plane."

"What fucking plane?"

"You're being deported"

The last thing they wanted was being back in Blighty. But they had no choice.

Back at Heathrow, three of them were arrested and sent to HMP Brixton. Great, that was what they were running from. Now they had to face the charges they were avoiding by going to Tenerife.

I got my solicitor to visit me and to commission a good barrister for my defence. QC Stephen Orlando

Parnell was the muttz nuttz. £1500 a day plus VAT. Well, being on a murder/manslaughter charge you need decent representation.

The first time at the Old Bailey, much to my surprise, I was presented with an attempted murder rap. So the geezer had lived, result!

At the first appearance, there was no evidence offered from the cops, obviously playing for time. Whilst still banged up in Brixton nick, the brief made a visit to tell me the good news. Whilst he was on the trot, a major investigation into police corruption was being carried out by the Thames Valley cops and most of the Lambeth CID had been suspended, hence no one to give evidence against me. Fiesta!! I was released at the next court appearance.

Luck was on my side again.

LGW - TFS

Being deported from Tenerife, after my release
from Santa Cruz prison with my passport having
the notorious red stamp in the back, I had to find a
way to get back to the island. Well, there was such a
thing in those days called the BVP. Here's the official
description of a British Visitors Passport.

*The BVP was a simplified version of the standard
passport, introduced in March 1961 and made available
to any British citizen. It was in the form of a 3-fold card
and could be obtained from any post office on sight
of the applicant's birth certificate or other specified
documents of identity. It was intended solely for a
holiday to specified European countries and was valid
for one year only. Due to many concerns arising in
connection with the easy availability and security of this
document, the BVP was withdrawn with effect from 1st of
January 1996.*

Well I knew someone in the Post Office, so I paid my
£12.50 plus a pint down the pub later, no ID required! I
was now travelling as Toby Lee.

I needed to get back to the island, as I had bought
a mountain finca whilst living there, an old place that
needed a lot a work to make it liveable. I had tried to get
it refurbished, but every time the materials were paid for
and delivered, they were stolen. The Spanish builders
would always arrive a week late and ask where the
materials were. In Spain you never know when *mañana*

will come! Unless I was to sit up there on mountain without any amenities for a week or more, it wasn't getting done. Now, no longer living on the island, it was time to sell it.

Arriving back at the new Queen Sofía airport, I got a taxi to Los Cristianos and booked into an apartment near the *playa*. It felt good being back in a warm country again. Even though the days in the winter could be sunny, cloudy or wet, the nights were never less than sixteen degrees. I went to a restaurant that I had used a lot before and ordered a *paella de marisco*. This seafood version of the famous rice dish was covered in massive prawns, it was right up my street. After, I went to a club I had frequently used in other trips, before finally collapsing back in my apartment for the night. It was a warm December night in the Canaries.

The next morning, I went straight to the estate agents that I had used before. I needed to get outa holiday mode and get me gaff sold. There was about thirty *casas* or *fincas* in the little village of Chimiche and my casa was number twenty seven, a number to repeat many times in my life.

The estate agent was very optimistic about a quick sale, the opening of the new Southern Airport had made the area a lot more interesting to property buyers. I couldn't believe that the next day there was an offer on my finca for nearly double what I had paid for it, before expenses. I decided to take it and run, so to speak. The agents nicked a couple a bob out of it and put the rest into my Spanish account, well eventually, nothing happens fast in Spain. Hunky-dory!

I thought it would be good to get some Christmas presents whilst I was there. In Spain they wrapped up any gift you bought and put on bows etc., if you said it was a present.

Dinero winging its way into my account, I decided to head home, having got the local barman to book a flight. It was sorted.

I arrived at the new airport to find out my flight was delayed for two hours, so I went to the duty free and bought the limit of fags and booze allowed. With two hundred fags you got a quarter bottle of Dewar's whisky. Then what else could I do but sit at the bar. By the time the plane had arrived I was three parts to the wind, I just managed to climb the steps to the plane.

By the time I reached Gatwick, I had little patience left. At the customs I was confronted by a little Pakistani and a big Jamaican. They started unwrapping my prettily wrapped presents, which was pissing me off, these were the Christmas presents for my family, but I half understood it. Then they started meticulously checking my booze and fag allowance.

"This quarter of whisky is over your allowance", said the Pakistani.

"But it's a pressy for my Granny, I didn't buy it, it came free wiv the oilys." I said.

"In this country you may only bring in two litres of alcohol." said the Pakistani. This pissed me off even more, but I still kept my cool.

I left the departures lounge into the main area well pissed off, in front of me was the information desk.

"Excuse me Sir, can the customs take booze off me wivout a receipt?"

"No, you should always get a receipt and you sign their copy."

Now I was fuming! I turned round and walked back in through the departures door and to the customs.

On arrival to the desk, I walked behind the counter

and saw the whisky. The big Jamaican tried to stop me but nothing was stopping me now. Someone had pressed the alarm button an Old Bill were coming from all directions blowing their whistles. I realised that I wasn't getting my whisky, so not wanting to let the thieving customs men have it, I took off the top and poured it all over the desk. Just seconds before half a dozen filth had thrown me to the deck and cuffed me. I was frogmarched to a cell and uncuffed, the door slamming in my boat race. Minutes later, Customs Officer Thomas, the 6'5" Jamaican, opened the peter slammer.

"You better not mention about leaving the desk without a receipt." said the big james hunt, staring down at me in a threatening manner.

"Well, what YOU gonna do about it then!" I said enraged, jumping up and making a rush for the officer. The big bully shit himself and slammed the peter door in my boat again. What a big coward I thought, I never saw him again.

A few minutes later a different copper opened the big steel slammer.

"My gov'nor wants to speak to you, come on."

"Look 'ere geezer, I don't speak to no filth wivout me brief, get that?"

Without another word the Old Bill left but returned minutes later.

"My gov'nor said he will phone you a Duty Solicitor in the morning."

"I don't want no 'kin Duty Solicitor, I wan MY 'kin brief!" I screamed.

The copper returned toting pen and pad.

"What's your brief's number?"

I knew Stew's office number and his home number in case of emergencies. Well this was definitely an emergency, and this time of night he would have his feet up by the fire. I reeled off the brief's home number.

I got my barnet on the pillow and was having a well needed kip when the door swung open. I didn't know how long I had been akip for, but when I opened my eyes, I was looking into the face of the lovely Stewy.

"Well I was just going to bed when the phone rang, only you would phone me at that unearthly hour. Listen now, I've had a chat with the Chief Officer and your going to be charged with defacing the Queen's property."

"The Queen's property?"

"Everything on the desk that you poured whisky all over, is the property of Her Majesty's Customs and Excise Service, hence the Queen's property. Anyway why would you want to do such a thing?"

Stewart sat on the bed whilst I told him the story. I always told my brief the absolute truth and then let the professionals spin a tale accordingly.

"So you didn't sign anything at all about relinquishing the bottle of whisky."

"No way, Jose!"

"Great, now I have something to work on. I'll go chat with the Chief and I'll let you know what's going on later."

"Cheers Stew!"

I was wide awake now. It seemed hours since that Stewart had been gone, then I noticed a slight glimmer of light coming from the little window high up on the cell wall. It was a new morning and like many mornings, I was waking up behind a big steel door again.

As I was thinking about it, the big steel door swung open.

"It's OK Officer, you can leave me here with the prisoner."

"Are you sure Sir, he's bit of a handful!"

"Don't worry, lock us in and I will ring the bell when I'm ready."

The door was shut quietly, not the usual slam. Stew was not saying a word until he could hear the noise of the coppers boots disappearing into the distance.

"The Chief wants to see you in person to give you a reprieve. I had to threaten to report officers Patel and Thomas for unprofessional conduct, to enable a deal whereby your are no longer getting charged. We now have to wait to be escorted back to the Chief's office."

Eventually two officers turned up and cuffed me, which is normal when in front of a Senior Officer and we were escorted to the Chief's office.

The Chief said he had studied the case and had decided not to press charges. I got had to go back to my peter and sign some papers, after which I would be released. So back we went and I was uncuffed. I sat on my bed with Stewy discussing another ongoing case we had running, back on the Manor. Eventually the paperwork arrived and after close perusal by my brief, I signed them.

"Your free to go now." said Mr Plod.

"What's the time Stewy?"

"6:40, why?"

"Well, anybody being held in a Police Station after 6am is entitled to a breakfast and I'm not going 'til I get mine. I know the law."

"Charlie!" Shouted the brief. "I'm waiting to take you home."

I said nothing but continued to stare at the plod, who eventually disappeared, no doubt to ask a senior officer if it was true.

Stewart and I sat in silence until the door opened again, this time the same Mr Plod came in holding a plastic plate with an egg sandwich on it.

"That's a sandwich not a fuckin' breakfast! You best try again!"

Stew got up and muttered something about getting himself a breakfast and stormed out. Not a happy bunny. About thirty minutes later, egg, bacon and beans, served with a slice of uncle fred, arrived.

"Where's my cuppa then?"

The plod just looked at me and walked out. He returned again fifteen minutes later holding a plastic mug of tea.

"I'll be back in ten minutes, your brief is waiting in the corridor by the front door."

An irate looking Stewart was waiting by the door.

"Only you Charlie!"

We had reached London before the brief was talking to me again.

The Fire Brigade strike

The first ever national strike by firefighters lasted nine weeks, from November 1977 to January 1978. During the strike, the army was drafted in to fight fires, using the fleet of 1950s 'Green Goddess' fire engines. Their use was limited compared to the modern day engine.

These slow machines had to come a fair distance in some circumstances and could only squirt water when they got there.

I offered to have an oxy-acetylene setup strapped to the back of a small lorry I had, parked up and ready on call when necessary.

It was Xmas day and the local pubs were rocking. We had had a good sesh in the Paxton and I had gone home on time, for a change, for the family Xmas dinner.

Before I had even got my boots off, a cop car screeched to a halt outside my front door. What had I done now, I was pissed but wasn't driving, I was indoors and I hadn't hit anything on the way home. What is was all this about on Xmas day? They were now pounding on my front door. I opened it to be confronted by two agitated cops.

"Quick get in the car! I'll explain on the way."

"On the way where Guv?"

I unhappily got in the cop car, to hear there had been a serious accident at the top of the road. A Rover 3 litre had mounted a Mini, trapping the two people inside and they needed my assistance. The sirens were turned on and we went up my street at great speed, the returning neighbours looked on in shock, what had Charlie done now?

In no time at all we were at my yard. I jumped into the old hijab truck and followed the cop car, sirens still screaming. I'd never had police escort before!

The big Rover had left the car park outside the Two Towers pub, obviously without looking and had mounted the little Mini from the front, crushing in the roof so badly that the rescuers were unable to open the doors.

By the time I had arrived, the Rover had been rolled off and the driver was sat in the back of one of the many cop cars. An ambulance soon arrived but nothing could be done.

I realised that this had be done right, working with a raw flame, an electrical or petrol fire would endanger the occupants even more.

"Cut the roof off," the Chief Officer commanded me.

"No, I have to take precautions first, I know what I'm doing!" I shouted at the cop with all the brass badges.

He said no more and I got my oxy-acetylene ready and then forced open the bonnet.

"Get a fire extinguisher ready please an' stand by me." A cop followed my orders, now I was running the show!

I turned the flame really low and carefully melted the lead that held the battery leads on.

"Now take the battery out and give the engine a good dose of your extinguisher."

That done, I put the bonnet back down and proceeded to cut through the door pillars, careful not to burn the old man driver and the young girl in the back seat of the little car. There was another problem stopping them getting out, the driver's seat had been crushed into the rib cage of the girl in the back, she didn't look good.

The obvious thing to do was to get the driver out first and then remove the seat, this was a problem as well, as the brake pedal was embedded into his leg. So I carefully cut the pedal off as high up as I could get.

A second ambulance had now arrived and the crew were looking at the old man.

"He will have many injuries and we must be very careful with him, in case his spine is one of them. Can you cut the seat out, so we can take him to the ambulance sat as he is, please."

I proceeded to cut through the rails that the seat pivoted on and once it was free, they carried him to the ambulance and drove off. I stepped to one side and left the other ambulance crew to attend the girl. She was soon in the other ambulance and gone too, she was constantly wailing the whole time I was there, she must have been in immense pain.

"Put the cars on the back of your truck an' take them back to your yard!" The Chief was back in charge again.

"Put them to one side where nobody can touch them, you hear?"

"Yes boss."

The Rover was easy to get on the truck, it still had door pillars but the Mini had to be strapped underneath and guided onto the back of the Ford. Looking on the back seat after, I spotted the entire contents of a full Xmas dinner, so sad. She was obviously sat in the back seat to stop it from spilling. It was now spread all round the back of the car.

Well even my yard dogs were getting Xmas dinner this year!

The next day, a group of cops came down the yard to take photos of the wrecks and take notes. They gave me the lowdown.

Paul, the son of a well known local family, had failed the breathalyser and had been charged accordingly. He wasn't used to drinking, unlike most boys around there, and had lost control of his powerful car.

The driver of the Mini, who was 69 years old, was in hospital with multiple but not life threatening injuries. The young lass was a dancer and I was told she would never dance again, her injuries were more complicated. What a terrible Xmas for that poor family.

There was only one more time the cops called me out. They needed a breakdown truck on New Year's Day and the regular contractor was not on the end of the phone. It was about five hundred yards from my yard, so I agreed to help. They promised I would get paid well for it, even the better!

I went and got the breakdown truck out and drove to the scene of the accident. It was obvious what had happened. The worst hit car had the drivers door caved in where he had jumped the lights on this big junction at Crown Point, West Norwood. They were soon removed and went into storage in my yard.

Apparently, the driver of the Escort, who's door was caved in, was taken to the hospital. The cop in charge had asked me to stay in the yard with the cars until the junction was clear, so he could check them.

I had a big old lurcher dog that had to check every car that came in the yard. These cars were no exception and he got lucky this time, the driver had obviously been to the butchers, as the old dog came out with a nice joint of meat, he proudly carried it to his kennel and sat there enjoying it.

About an hour later, whilst the cops were taking their

notes, an ambulance arrived, they had come to find the man's calf, apparently it had been sheared off in the accident.

"I ain't seen nuffin' Guv!"

It was the good old days before they abolished the yearly passport

The new yearly passport had opened a new way of going into anywhere in Europe and commit any crime we wanted, in any name. All you had to do was go down to the local post office, show them some form of ID and for £12.50 you had a valid passport for a year. Well, I knew people in the local post office, so I could be who I wanted to be.

The gun smuggling was going well but ammunition was becoming a better line, now that they were all tooled up. I decided that an ammo run was on the cards.

One day I took Mad Mick down to the local post office and I bought two new yearly passports. I was Toby Lee and he was Michael Lee. We had just the day before bought full length leather coats off a blagger. Mine was black and Mick's was brown. I got some money from under my floorboards and we caught a taxi to the Brighton ferry. Can you imagine what a taxi from London to the Brighton Ferry would cost. It's sixty five miles, I'm sure I would have cracked on with some kind of deal with the driver.

When we got to the ferry office, we had to get our passports checked. I passed them through a hole in the window and they were forever coming back. People were coming and going but our passports weren't coming back. After about fifteen minutes, I thought it was on top when a pleasant young lady appeared at the window, "Sorry to keep you waiting." And smiled, passing them back. Phew!!

We had a few on the ferry, well what else was there to do, and when it docked, we found a fisherman's bar locally and finished the sesh. The bar was full of Ricard anisette drinkers, they seemed to be living in a different world to us. We had a few Calvados and hit the street looking for accommodation. There were thousands of houses advertising accommodation in Dieppe. We walked for miles but all the doors we knocked on were answered wit a blunt *non*. Then we come across a door with a lit up Stella sign hanging above. The door was opened by a brassy old bird about fifty. "You drinking Champagne?" she said.

"I'll drink anyfing to get off the street," I said and we was let in. I thought it must be a knocking shop but I was wrong, all this old bird wanted was to sell Champagne to us, she could put it away fast herself. Of course we were footing the bill. I made eyes at the young barmaid but the old biddy met my eyes with a definite NO! It felt strange, a situation I was never in before. When we reached tilt, she phoned a cab who took us to a two-star hotel. Now that was what we wanted. A bed for the night, but what was strange was we were given a double! Did we look like a pair a turd burglers? Then to prove them wrong we phoned for "un femme." They bought us up a tray of nice turkey sandwiches. We gave up, and got a well needed kip.

Next morning we went down to the breakfast room but it was basically just bread, croissants and jam! The French didn't understand what proper breakfast was.

I called for a taxi to take us out to the country to find the little gun shop that I used. Here we could buy what we wanted, and that's what we did. I had seen the last time I was here a pretty little 38mm Special, a sort of powerful handbag tool with a carved ivory stock, so this time I bought it. Micky on the other hand fancied a long barrelled 9mm. These pieces now hid on our bodies, we filled the cases with ammo. Things were good.

We always booked cabins coming back. Mick was up the jump getting pissed an I decided to go back to the cabin. I stayed there until we were docking, I didn't want part of what Mike was doing. He was a good loyal friend but he would sometimes go that extra mile when I would just want to hide. Hence Mick was pissed and going wild in the bar and I was taking a kip in our cabin.

Mick burst through the cabin door, hardly able to stand.

"They're docking, they're docking!"

"Ya as pissed as a parrot Mick, you need to shape up, we have these two cases to carry through customs now. Drink that bottle of water over there." I said pointing to a litre bottle on the bedside table.

"I've enough to drink already." He slurred.

"I can see that, down that water now! Ya'll get us both nicked!"

We went out onto the deck, where there was already a big queue waiting to disembark. We were at the back and it seemed like forever. As the queue shortened I noticed there were a lot of obvious cops, all wearing identical blue coats with their right mitts stuck under their armpits . They stuck out like a sore thumb. These were no ordinary cops, they looked more like the Terrorist Squad. I pointed them out to Mick.

"Someone is in big trouble here today, that's a serious squad, all tooled up. Look." I said.

Well, the ferry was nearly all unloaded and they were

still there. I couldn't make it out.

As we disembarked, they grabbed us, thrust guns in our boat races and escorted us to a quayside wharf.

A tall, well spoken man went away with our passports. Meanwhile, a short Scotsman in a grey suit pointed to Mick,

"Who's the clever one who threatened the barman with a pistol then, was it you?"

"Yes Boss."

"Empty your pockets on the table, both of you."

We did as instructed but there was nothing incriminating on our persons, until they rubbed us down and Mick still had his 9mm down his pants.

"We're just going to have a quick look at your dirty laundry whilst we wait for the Boss to return."

They opened the cases and didn't seem at all surprised at what they found. They just did them back up and we waited for the main man.

He eventually appeared back in wharf.

"Shall I call you Toby or Charlie?" He said to me. He definitely had us tumbled. "Sam, go get the Customs men, the rest of you come with me, these are only small fry, they are of no interest to us."

And they disappeared leaving me with my mouth open, who's he calling fucking 'small fry', how dare he!

In marched the Customs men, all super efficient, they even stripped us naked and looked up our arses. Hold tight, we have two suitcases full of guns and ammunition, why the fuck would we be hiding anything up our bottles? Just showed the mentality of these men.

When we were dressed again, the Customs men picked up the two cases and we were escorted through the 'Nothing to Declare' and into the charging office. Here, we were charged with 'Importing Firearms and

Explosives without a licence to do so'. We were bailed on our own recognizance for the sum of £2000, but we would only have to pay that if we failed to turn up at court.

I won't say I was a very happy bunny on the way home. In fact I was fuming.

"Why the fuck did you have to stick ya tool in the barman's boat race?"

"He refused to serve me, he said I was too drunk already."

"So that drink is gonna cost me an' you a five stretch min?"

"Sorry Char!"

I said no more, I just sat there in silence, I had not only just lost a fair few bobs worth of grub, what we call ammo, but I was also about to lose my liberty.

I went back to work the next day, as normal. I now just had to wait for a court date, meanwhile life has to go on. We had plenty to do, to make up for the money that I lost.

A week went past and two local cops, George and Ginger George, came prancing into the yard. It wasn't an unusual sight, they both had Cortinas, and they always came to ponce spares off me.

"You one lucky motherfucker Breaker!" said the ginger one.

"Whatcha mean Gez?"

"Stupid poxy Customs twats!"

I knew the cops and customs didn't get on but what was this about.

"When you got arrested coming off the ferry, who carried the cases through the 'Nothing to Declare'?"

"Well I guess they did George, why?"

"They didn't give you the chance to declare them,

so you haven't broke the law! You lucky pair a motherfuckers. Stupid fucking Customs!"

They left the yard laughing and we burst into laughter as well.

We had a party in The Paxton Inn that night.

Dodgy Notes

In the '70s some dodgy £5s had hit the market. Being the first of a kind, they were easy, nobody knew that such a thing existed.

I'd never worked them myself but liked to buy a lot and bulk them out. For some reason, I never fancied doing them in the shops or pubs, that I frequented. I think firstly that I was careful how I treated the people in my life, including the businesses I used. I also think I was scared of embarrassing myself.

£5s an £10s made regular appearances, so much so, that the people taking them were starting to check the feel of the paper and running their fingers across the top left of the note, feeling for the serrations.

Eventually the £20s made a brave debut, these were definitely gonna get checked.

One day I got a visit from the best man around about fraud or banknote crime. It was Bitter Lemon Bob, so called because even though he spent a lot of time in the pubs, that was only what he ever drank!

We sat down for a bit of a chat and he educated me in the new ways to keep up with increasing vigilance of the public towards the banknotes.

He had a large consignment of the new £20s for me. He then described to me about washing the notes with a 10% Comfort, 90% warm water solution. Then crumpling them up, to make them look like they had been around the block a few times, and hanging them out to dry.

But before this softening treatment, there was one more thing to do. Because more and more of the shop girls were being taught to feel for the serrations along the top of the note, summit had to be done. So he showed me how to put the note over a hand held nutmeg grinder and run my finger firmly over it. The firm serration that ensued after was softened by the Comfort and felt more realistic.

The first batch done and it started pissing it down before I could hang them out on the washing line. So I decided to lay them out on the big old Rayburn that I had in my country house kitchen. The Rayburn had the ability of warming the water, heating the house, having a permanent hot oven, a hot box to warm the plates and six hobs on the top. Now I had found another function, I could squeeze a hundred wet notes on the top at a time, completely drying them in about 20 minutes. They turned out fine.

The next morning "the sun had its hat on an' was coming out to play". I opened up the kitchen windows to see the first inch or two of the daffodils pushing their way through the soft wet soil and the birds singing merrily, heralding the beginning of spring.

It wasn't long before hundreds of crumpled £20s were blowing in the calm hot wind, no clothes were gonna get dried today! I went in to finish off another batch ready to go out.

Suddenly I could hear the unmistakable laughter of my best pal, Mark Ripleys. Looking out the kitchen windows I could see him coming up my long driveway. The dogs were going mad with the excitement, Mark loved the dogs and they loved him. "Hey Charl what a sight! I love it."

Mark loved crime as much as I did. When you loved

it as much we did, it was a joy to see it happening.

"Hi Mate, I have you eaten?" I said remembering my stove was free again.

"I could eat a scabby horse!"

I pulled out a slab of salted bacon and carved some thick rashers, these were soon in the pan with whatever else was to hand. We took our breakfasts out into the front garden to eat. It really was turning out to be a nice day. At last winter was leaving us.

"I'm going to The Pheasant in Orpington tonight, fancy it?"

I'd never been there before, although we'd passed it many times.

"There's a lot a Chambers use it don't they?"

"That's why I'm going there tonite, to see little Barry Chambers and Irish Mary. She's been paid out for her scar an' Barry wants a muck away tipper. I got jus' the thing for him."

We spent most of the day sat out there in the garden, watching the first brood of Old English Game chicks scratching around in the meadow, amongst the many other birds an animals I kept those days.

We decided to have a quick one at the Amazon & Tiger pub in Harvel Village before going up town. I stuffed handful of notes in my pockets, in case we bumped into anyone who wanted a sample.

We arrived to see the pub already busy, quite a few needies were up at bar. Snobby's Tony Rossiter, Pear Brazil and his son Mark amongst them.

"Gissus one of them 20s Charl, I'll get a round."

"Not here Mark it's me local, I'll get them."

Before we had finished talking, Pear was already up the jump and had ordered, ours as well. We didn't stay long before we hit the M20 to go to Orpington.

When we arrived at the Pheasant, it was packed with travellers, mostly young Chambers and a few from Swan lane.

"Gissus one a them 20s Charl!"

I passed him one and he bought a few drinks for those in our company. Well, he kept doing it all night. The Guv'nor was either stupid or scared to say anything, it was so obvious.

After, we were hank marvin and we went looking for a kebab shop. We soon found one and ordered two large donnas. Mark went to pay, I said no it's my turn. This was the normal argument between us, but this time it was for summit different. I wanted to do my first note!

Now I had done one, there was no stopping me when I was out of my area, you don't shit in your own back yard. The next night I was meeting little Scotch Dougie and five of us were going up the West End. I loaded up my pockets before we left.

Once we had settled into a big club, we found a runner boy to do the bar for us. He took 20 after 20 all night to the busy bar. Flashing the cash we were soon surrounded by girls.

Picking a girl each, when the club shut, we decided to go to Chinatown and have a meal in one of their 24h restaurants.

"A table for ten please!"

"We only have one it's on the fifth floor."

We made our way up the narrow staircase to the top floor. A waiter arrived with the menu and disappeared. As if he had read our minds he reappeared just as we had made up ours.

We ordered and it all arrived soon including ten bottles of wine, one each!

We sat there and the more pissed we got, the louder

we became. Eventually it was decided to take our richards home whilst we were still capable. Someone called for the bill.

When it came, I piled all the money in 20s with a good £10 on top and we started to make it down the stairs. By the time we got to the 3rd floor there was lots of screaming Chinese running about wanting to kill us. We just run like fuck across town to where the cars were and escaped back to South London. That was a close one!

After that weekend, I decided that it wasn't good for me working them myself, if I got took, they would have reason to raid my house and find boxes of them. It was a good weekend though!

It was the year after Mark died and I was getting back up on my feet again. I'd had a quiet winter, I lost a lot of enthusiasm when I lost Mark. It was to be the last time I'd see Bitter Lemon Bob as well, before he died.

He turned up with one crisp £50. Perhaps, even though very new looking, they were the best snides yet.

"Hi Bob, how the fuck can we work 50s? As they go into the bank, the bells will start ringing. It will be on the front pages nationwide."

"No Charlie boy, they're not coming out 'til after the banks are shut on Easter Thursday. You have then Friday, Saturday, Sunday and Monday to work them, before the banks reopen. I will leave this one sample to get orders with, don't part with it for fuck's sake! You've got ten days to get the orders with me, for delivery Thursday afternoon."

I had a brilliant idea. You could go to the bank and get £2,500 in a sealed bag, all brand new notes. I had a little Maltese bird working in a local bank and she could get a load of these bags for me and I could seal the dodgy £2500 with a household iron. Ideal for big Gipsy horse deals in the Easter Horse Fairs. These guys thought nothing on spending £30k on the right horse. Twelve bags from me and they could get a cheap horse.

By Easter I had taken deposits on nearly 2 million in dodgies. What a good weekend. That was the one and only £50 scam ever, you can't do these twice.

The Body in the Boot case

Me and Mark worked from a big piece of land at the top of Knight's Hill in West Norwood.

What happened was, going back to the Jubilee year of '77, I had squatted an old factory and about half an acre of land. It belonged to an absent West African. He had no interest in its use but had obviously bought it as a long term investment. We used the factory as a workshop and had filled up the yard with scrapers.

There was a pub over the road, called The Crown, where we always went for lunch. We'd leave the gates open and a boy keeping watch for punters. One day the boy rushed in the pub.

"Charlie, the black man from the tyre shop over the road, has jus' walked into the yard and took two tyres."

"OK Mickey, go back to the yard, we'll be back in a minute."

Mark and I finished off our pints and went back over to the yard. Sure enough, two of the four near new Rover wheels and tyres were gone. I'd just bought them off the back of Jimmy Pillock's old J-type Harvey Frost only an hour earlier.

"Right I'll deal wiv this, you two stay here."

I crossed the road to the tyre shop to confront the Jamaican. Giving him chance to pay for them, I asked,

"Did you jus' pick two Rover wheels outa me yard?"

"No, me don't know wha' ya chat 'bout!"

I looked around the shop and couldn't see them, so I pushed him to one side and opened the door to the store room and there they were. I spun round, put a good right into his boat race just above his left mince pie and left the shop with a wheel in each hand.

About half hour later, the local cops arrested me for assault and took me to the cop shop. There he was, the dirty grass, sporting a massive swelling over his left mince. I don't know how it works but if you catch someone on the bone at the end of the eyebrow, it can have that effect. It like wearing a kids football on the side of ya boat.

"You not only wanna rob me wheels, but now ya wanna grass me up, you dirty slag!" I shouted.

The cops gently coerced me into a cell and I remained there, having a quick kip until they finally woke me, to tell me that 'Berty Smalls' had left the premises.

I was taken to the charging desk to face Sgt. Smith, a wise old copper I had faced many times across this same desk.

"Right, you know the routine, empty your pockets an' off with your boots an' belt."

"Yes Sarge."

As I emptied my pockets, I suddenly realised that I had a book of blank MOTs I had bought that morning, in my back pocket.

"Oh dear Charlie what have got here?"

"I found them in an old scrapper I bought this morning Sarge, an' I was gonna bring 'em up to you after work tonight."

"Of course you were." said the Sargent sarcastically. "Well we saved you the petrol money."

The coppers behind me let out a little snigger and only then did the Sarge look up from his desk to glare at them and then turn back towards me.

"Charlie you will need to go back to your new home, whilst I sort out the new charge."

"Take him away men."

One stupid young cop went to hold my arm, I pushed it off, he got the message.

I got another quick kip before I was back out at the charging desk again. I was charged with GBH section 18 with intent and handling the proceeds of a robbery.

"Well now you can charge the spoof for stealing your wheels and tyres." Said the Sargent.

"I ain't no dirty grass Gov!"

"I was expecting a reply like that, go on, off you go."

Oh well another day off to go to Camberwell Green Magistrate's Court coming up. These days, when on the lesser charges, I always ended up afterwards going on the piss in The Father Redcap or The Silver Buckle, both on the Green.

I was working with the oxy-acetylene cutting gun one day, when a smartly dressed man entered the yard carrying a briefcase. I turned off the gas and confronted the stranger. I knew all the local CID and this wasn't one one them.

"Morning Sir, can I help you?"

"My names Mike Perot, I'm the borough valuer for Lambeth Council."

"What can I do for you Mr Borough Valuer?"

"It's about the land."

"Well it ain't my land, it belongs to Nigerian, who's gone back to Africa."

"Well it did, it now belongs to Lambeth Council."

"Did you buy it off him then Guv?"

"No, we sent him a Compulsory Purchase Order and he chose to ignore it. So we applied to the courts and successfully gained a Compulsory Possession Order."

I hadn't got a clue about these things. Mr Perot put his briefcase down on the bonnet of a car and produced from it a paper labelled across the top PO 113.

"See if anybody choses not to agree to our offer for their land, we have this option up our sleeve and we need this land to add to the piece we own next door for a building project."

"So we're on your land, your saying?"

"I'm afraid so!"

"But Mr Perot we can't move overnight, we have a lot a stock here and we need somewhere to take it all."

"I've already got that in hand. There's an old railway siding not far from here in Sainsbury Rd. There's plenty of room there for you and you can stay there until we need it sometime next year. We've cleared it off but we need it occupied to keep the 'fly shooters' from tipping their 'muck away' illegally."

"It's already occupied by Teddy Mitchell!"

"I know, but it's a big yard and Mr Mitchell is only using a small part. You can spread your wings on the other side."

"How much is all this gonna be?"

"As long as you play ball with me, it won't cost you anything, not even council tax."

"OK you have a deal." I said, putting out a greasy hand, which the council man shook, before he realised his mistake.

Looking down at his dirty hands, he said "What is your name?"

"Charlie."

The Borough Valuer looked across at a big man sat cross legged on the ground, cooking his breakfast in an upturned Bedford J-type hubcap, balanced on a circle of rocks, hiding a fire.

"And this other man?"

"That's my mate Paulie."

"Do you have a phone?"

"No."

"Well, I'll pop in from time to time."

After handing me his card, out walked the Council man. He was a good connection to have and would no doubt come in useful in the future. He was a man to be looked after.

We started loading the long nosed Thames Trader that day, only the day before had I bought it from Wally Coates from The Lonesome Depot site. Things were going right for a change.

That night we met up with the Mitchell's in the Two Towers pub. Teddy was in there with his two boys and a good night was had by all. In fact it got so loud that Mary, the guv'nor Pat McGuinness' wife, had to ask us to be quiet.

Mind you she was a stipler, unlike Pat, when she was in the bar, no swearing, no singing. Even laughter was considered a cardinal sin!

The next day Mark turned up in his 'thupenny bit', as the BMC lorrys were know as in those days. He soon got told the news.

"Mark, as I cut out what I wanna keep, you can load the rest on ya truck an' take it to Henry Dixie's."

Mark, Paulie and Mark's son Tarzan, loaded the truck three times in one day and got two delivered to Dixie's Iron Yard. A good days work. Not to underestimate Tarzy, this young fella who, if he ever went to school would still be in a Junior class, could pick up a small car engine on his own and load it on the truck. Mother die, you wouldn't Adam 'n' Eve it, unless you see it for yourself!

We soon settled into our new more prominent position, it was a lot better situation. Eddie was a great guy to have as a neighbour, we got on so well that one day he arrived with a deerhound cross greyhound pup as a present for me, that dog went to work with me everyday of the week for many years.

Teddy had his fingers in a few pies and he had this lump work for him, called Frank, whose hands were bigger than his brain. Teddy supplied him with a big green Vauxhall Cresta, the 3 litre one with a wrap round windscreen. They were powerful and were a favourite choice as getaway cars.

One night it had gone out over the police radio that there had been a robbery locally and the getaway car was a green Cresta. By coincidence, big Frank was just on his way home from the pub.

Just before he reached home he was surrounded by cop cars, lights flashing and sirens screaming. He got out of the car and was immediately cuffed and thrown in the back of a big black Austin Westminster, the choice car for the upper ranks of the Met.

The cops opened the boot to find, not the loot they expected, but a stiff, obviously been there for several days. Frank was taken back to the cop shop and charged with first degree murder.

Apparently Frank was visiting someone over a debt and he got a bit heavy handed. Not knowing what to do, he put the body in the boot.

Next day I went to work to find 2 JCBs being unloaded in the street. Then a big 4 wheel drive forklift. I couldn't make out what was happening. I was even more mystified when the cop cars, marked and unmarked, pulled into the yard. Then an unmarked

Range Rover arrived. The driver jumped out, opened a back door to let out an important looking CID officer, who waded through to mud towards me.

"Someone arrest this man!" He shouted, pointing at me.

I was surrounded by uniformed cops who cuffed me and took me to Streatham nick. As we pulled out of the yard, another van arrived with the first clue. On the side it displayed....

'HOMICIDE INVESTIGATION UNIT'

So, someone had been murdered, but what did that have to do with me or these old railway sidings?

Back at the nick, I was thrown into a cell and left there for hours. Eventually I was put in front of the DCI that had arrived in the yard in Range Rover. In the room there were two more CID standing by the desk.

"Right, we know who you are but we need to know more about what goes on in this yard your using. Let's start with who's Mr Mitchell to you?"

"I don't know a Mr Mitchell."

"Teddy Mitchell you share the yard with."

"Oh him, I don't really know him. Me an' Teddy don't talk, I don't fink he likes me."

"Your not being very helpful, you could be in here a long time."

"I could do wiv a rest Guv'nor."

"How do you fancy a five stretch for criminal association? Now co-operate!"

"Who's Frank Gardener?"

"I don't know boss."

"Show him a mugshot Sargent."

Of course I knew who he was, he was a well known local thug, best to keep away from. He could empty a bar, just by walking through the door. Everybody knew

Frank.

"I've seen him around, Boss."

"Around the yard perhaps?"

"I've not seen him there but then I've not been in that yard long."

"Show him the car Sargent."

"What do you know about this car?"

"Now you me got me on summit I know all about."

"Go on tell me." Said the DCI looking a bit happier now.

"It a green Vauxhall Cresta Mk 2, with a 3 litre straight six attached to a 4 speed box wiv overdrive. Anything else I can tell you?"

"Sargent, throw this bastard back in a cell and leave him there to rot!"

The DCI stormed out of the room.

Sure enough I was thrown back in the peter and got a lot more rest. In fact all day, all night until 10 the next morning. They had obviously given up on getting anything outa me!

10:30 that wet morning, I got out the cop car to see all me cars in a heap in the middle of the yard. Because of the mud, I had parked my drag in the street, if I hadn't, it would probably be in the pile with the rest. The whole yard had been dug up for everybody to see, and yes, they were all there, including reporters and photographers. People that knew me were asking me what happened, I couldn't get away from there quick enough.

The next day was Friday and The South London Press was out....

THE BODY IN THE BOOT FIRM WORKING FROM GIPSY HILL SIDINGS.

It was splattered across the front page, followed by

the full story of what happened. I couldn't go anywhere without being questioned, but I only knew what the press said.

Knight's Hill Breakers

I wasn't part of the body in the boot firm, but couldn't work from that yard again, or drink in the pubs too local, so I phoned Mike Perot.

If I was prepared to wait a week and fence up the yard at my own expense, he had a massive plot at the top of Knight's Hill where they were demolishing a big house with a lake in the garden. I went and looked at it and it was a great position and very big.

Not far away, they were taking down a lot of galvanized fencing ready for redevelopment. That night I took a couple of the local boys, my Thames Trader and Marks 'thrupenny bit' and we cleared all the sheets and posts between us. It was all stored in my garden, behind my own galvy fencing!

I was up there every day keeping a mince pie on the progress. I stayed away from the railway sidings. I didn't like not going to work but I'd rather that than being questioned all day by press and public.

Goodbye Gipsy Hill.

It was an exciting day when we arrived, Mark brought two dossers out of Orpington, I brought John Bird, Michael Oakes, Mad Mick and Taffy and put them on the firm. By the end of the day, the fence was up and the gate almost there.

Now we had a massive plot, an orchard backing onto the neighbours walls, which we left untouched, and about an acre of land that was divided by a big lake.

"How many 'muck aways' could we get in that lake?" said Mark, meaning 'fly shoots'.

He had point, we didn't need a lake in the middle of our yard. So……

Every day after then, nobody questioned the fact that there was a lot of water running down the hill. Every lorry load sent several square yards of water onto the hill. We were gaining space and earning, hunky-dory!!

When the lake was no more, we had almost doubled the size of the yard. Only one problem, the tipped area couldn't be drove on by our plant. We soon had a Smith 30 crane on tracks and a Wetheral shovel from a coal yard. The shovel was a heavy beast with a one ton bucket, it had the ends gone and a hydraulic problem. I gave £100 scrap for it, and within a week Mad Mick had it up and running. A couple of cans of Easystart, some rubbing down paper and a £10 part from the local hydraulics works. Blockhead he called it! It was his pride and joy, it had no PAS but he threw this 10 ton machine around the yard like Formula 1 car.

One day Mark walked in.

"I met this mush last night an' he has the contract to lose waste tarmac scrappings for Beech's. They are doing a lot of road resurfacing around the area. He's prepared to pay to dump them. Would they be any good for the lake?"

"Well if we get £5 a load it's worth a try Mark."

"I'll go down there tonight an' tell him he's welcome."

Next day, load after load of soft hot tarmac scrappings were tipped on the edge of the lake area. Mick was busy with Blockhead patting it down, using the big one ton coal bucket. It was still soft until it cooled down. Then it made a hard surface. Ideal!

The three acre site had a little orchard backing onto the posh neighbours' gardens at the rear. So it was decided to put the trailers there and keep the area free of scrap, trying to keep the posh people happy. This turned out to be impossible.

We put another old trailer by the gate, acting as an office and an escape from the weather. We cut the roof off an old Hillman Hunter, took the back seats out and used it as cart for the cutting bottles. John Bird was called in to build a dog run. It was all dropping into shape.

For over three years we filled it up with scrap, mostly cars. I controlled the buying and selling side and Mark was loaded up regularly by the Smiths' crane and driving it down to Dixie's yard. It was a good cover for a lot a crime, and a van load of loot could be put in a corner and hidden by a heap of scrap or a couple of cars.

Life was good and we were raking it in.

Then, one day Mike Perot walked in the yard, I took him into the office and shook his hand.

"Hello Mike, long time no see, what can I do for you."

"Charlie, the council want do some drilling in the yard, with the chance of some new houses being built on here one day, when they have the money."

"Mike they'll think they've struck oil, drilling in my yard. There's a layer of oil right through it! About a thousand cars a year come through here!"

We both sat and laughed a while, but it was a slightly nervous laugh, knowing what the next bit of conversation was going to entail.

"You see Charlie, we need the yard completely empty to do it."

"When is that for Mike?"

"I can give you a month."

"Shit, I have to find another yard, an' then move all this!" I said pointing out the window.

"Well, I have another yard for you, it's only about half a mile away but it's very small. You can put your plant in there and tick over but it's nowhere near the size of this place."

He discussed the whereabouts of the new yard to be. I knew exactly where it was.

"Now for the good news. They'll need it for about a month and when they're finished I will come tell you and you can come back."

"Phew, not so bad!"

"OK, but you must leave the fence up, to keep out the fly shooters out."

"OK Mike, I will phone you."

We shook hands again and Mike walked away looking pleased. I just sat there scratching my head, where did I start?

Leaning back, deep in thought, with me minces shut, my train of thought was broken by the sound of Mark's truck, being as the exhaust had fallen off, it couldn't be mistaken.

Mark jumped out the passenger side with Tarzy. Celia was driving and young Henry was in the cab.

"Hi mate, you fancy a bit a breakfast?"

"Always up for a bit a scram, you know me Char!"

"Load the family up in me Transit an' we're shav."

"Tarzy can help in the yard, we can bring him summit back." Said Mark.

Once we'd settled in the cafe, I told Mark the full SP.

"Well wiv this big Guy truck I got now, I can get five shells strapped on the back."

"I fink four will be safe M8!"

"Watch me!"

I knew now the challenge was on. If you told Mark he couldn't do it, he would shift the world to prove me wrong. We had our breakfasts and I ordered bacon sarnies for all the boys back up the yard. After dropping them off with Celia, we drove down to look at the new yard.

Right in the middle of Norwood High Street, it was completely walled with a big metal gate. Bolt cropping the chain, we were in. This was a very small place compared to the last one. There was enough room for the plant, the trailers and a couple a dozen cars. But there was one very interesting factor, the building that the council had dozed had a massive cellar, it was like an old woman with a big hole that needed filling! Of course the fly shooters were contacted immediately.

Their work was cut out now and much of it was cutting out the engines and gearboxes before Mark weighed the shells in. The shells fetched decent money down at Dixie's but the engine reconditioning factory in Bow paid a lot more for engines. So one at a time the cars were lifted by Ray the crane, on the Smith's 30 and the engines were cut out and then loaded on my old J3 Bedford. The shells were then loaded onto Marks Guy truck.

Three or four weeks later we were ready for the final manoeuvre. We would party all night in the yard and have a tyre fire.

You might wonder why a tyre fire. Well, in the few years we had occupied the yard, we had never burnt a tyre, except perhaps an old mini wheel and tyre to get the fire going in the 45gal oil drum, but after that it was the wood sides off of trucks we had. The problem was, the posh neighbours to the rear of us wanted us out, so they kept reporting us saying that we burned tyres in the yard. Bloody lies. It was get back time!

We had a mountain of bald tyres on steel wheels, probably about 25 feet tall. So on the last night after dark, we set fire to the rubber mountain. We sat there all night whilst it burnt, watching the black smoke engulf the posh detached houses at the back. There wouldn't be any happy bunnies there in the morning, when we were loading up all the wheels ready for delivery to Dixie's iron yard.

When we arrived at the new yard the next morning, there was already a small queue of muck away trucks waiting outside. Within five days the hole was filled and the land usable had doubled. Hunky-dory!

About a month went past and Mike Perot dropped in.

"You can go back up to Knight's Hill again now until further notice. When Lambeth council find the money, they will want to build but it won't be this year."

"Thanks Mike, is there any thing I can do for you?"

"All I need to know is that the land is in your control"

"No problems there Mike, thanks."

We shook german bands and Mr Perot left the yard.

EBT's Cafe was only a couple of doors down. Egg 'n' Bacon Tony was an old friend and we loved going there for breakfast. That's exactly what we done when Mark arrived.

The spirits were high, we couldn't wait to get back to our big yard. Back in our little yard we loaded anything we had with the old drags etc. Mark had his 7 ton Guy, with no exhaust, I had my Ford Custom cab with no windscreen and there were various other trucks waiting for export. Transits trucks to Malta and Bedford J-types to Africa. They were all loaded and the Exodus was ready.

When we arrived at our yard, the gates were open. What the fuck! So we drove in and there was an old tourer and a few scrappers parked in there. I jumped out and confronted a young geezer that was shitting himself.

"What's fuckin' happening here?"

"I'm jus' here lookin' after the yard for somebody."

"What fuckin' somebody?" Mark stepped in.

"I work for Micky Locke an' Dave Bishop."

"Yer I know them, they got Balham Breakers!"

"Yer that's right." said the frightened young fella.

"Right, well, you're looking after our trucks also, whilst we sort it out. Come on Char we'll go sort it."

The boys walked back to the little yard, whilst me and Mark walked back to EBT's, he had a dog 'n' bone.

It was time to get our little phone books out and get the ball rolling. Everyone Mark spoke to, he to told to share with as many travellers as possible. I did the same to my friends.

Within thirty minutes the first truck loads were arriving from Streatham. We waited until we had about five truck loads, all standing on the back and a few big cars full of local villains before we went to Balham Breakers. When we got there, Micky and Dave sent out a worker to see what was going on. Well that worker happened to be Matty Jones, a traveller and brother to a couple of boys I was in Brixton nick with, Jankeyes and Georgie Jones. About a hundred of us followed him back to the office. As Matty entered, they could see us through the window. Matty had without doubt marked their card with what they were facing.

"I've told my bosses who you are an' they will remove their stuff today. They didn't know the situation, but understand now."

Once again, the power overruled the ones that thought they could overrule everybody, even these well known Croydon villains.

Symes vs Stockings

In the early '80s, the owner of an apple orchard had split it into plots and sold them off to whoever was interested. It was in Gold Street, at the back of Hadlow Agricultural College. A beautiful location.

I got the details off Levy Smith, Mark's brother in law, and went and paid my money into a Croydon solicitor. I had no intention of moving there at the moment, but it was a nice weekend plot and beside an investment.

One day we were over Lewisham site on Loampit Hill, visiting the other travellers that lived there.

As we pulled up, so did Plob, Mark Baker, who I'd known since he was a boy. We crossed paths a lot in the boxing world. He was a successful Amateur and Professional Super Middleweight. He invited us in to meet his pretty Irish wife and chavies. We stopped for tea and moved on.

We noticed in the plot next door was a beautiful Vickers West Moreland Star. Parked in front was an immaculate Bedford TK. This was unmistakably the home of the well known Big Mick Johnson and his pretty little wife. I knocked but he wasn't in, so we moved down to the end plot to see Symie 'The Blacksmith' Doherty.

Symie welcomed us up to join him and his wife, Queenie. I'd never seen a woman wearing so much gold in my life. They had 13 children, but young Charlie was run over outside the site, and now only had 12. One of those young boys was a Patrick, the now famous Paddy Doherty of TV fame.

Symie told us that he shared the plot with his Brother Francis, and Francis Coyle. They had loads of chavies as well, including a little Tony Coyle.

These plots on the Lewisham site were divided into 4 separate plots. He explained that there was an empty one in the corner and he was looking to get someone in there before someone he didn't want was moved in by the council.

We were keen to get away from the attention of Streatham old bill, whilst still on the Lonesome Dept site. This was ideal and still in South London. We had a quick look, it was perfect.

We thanked Symie and went back to Streatham, pleased with the day's work.

The next day was Sunday, and after a visit to Barry Copes' seafood stall, we always went visiting. This day we were going to see Levy and Lilley in the orchard.

When we arrived at the orchard we could smell the apple blossom in the trees all around their trailer. As we sat outside on the ground, we absorbed in the pretty blossoms in the trees and the tunes of the finches singing. What a beautiful place to live.

Surely it couldn't get better, surrounded by beautiful trees, songfull birds, a couple of friendly lurchers, the lovely Lillie, her Levy and four polite chavies. Levy, the eldest, was the epitome of a well mannered boy, his two very pretty sisters Rosie and Pearlie, not forgetting young Joe, also a nice young fella.

Levy told me he had an Astral Luxi for sale. I had an Astral Ranger but the Luxi was a lot prettier.

Levy offered to take the Ranger in chop but I declined, I had other ideas. I would pay in cash in the morning. The hands were slapped and it was mine.

My idea was to move to Lewisham with the Luxi, leaving the Ranger on site, door open ready for the gavvers, if they visited. If I moved it, they would wonder where I was.

In the morning I was at the orchard paying Levy and hooking up to my new trailer. By lunchtime it was sited in Lewisham. Now to move my bits from The Lonesome.

On arrival at The Lonesome Dept, we were greeted by Kenny Symes, Linda looking on.

"You know what Amos Bill all about?"

We certainly did, we nodded.

"Well he's paying Jimmy Stocking to fight me next Saturday! Will you two see fair play?"

"Of course mate." We almost said in unison. "Where Ken?"

"Here at ten o'clock."

Fights were always arranged for 10am at a site somewhere.

"We'll be here. I'm moving my stuff today but leaving the trailer." I said.

I explained why, he understood all too well.

We hooked up Mark's spare trailer, an old Jubilee and moved to Lewisham.

When we arrived looking for Symie, we were told he was in the pub just over the road. The street was full of top of the range cars. We ventured in there. I've never seen such a rough house in my life, everyone wanted a fight with someone! It was full of Irish with an Irish Guv'nor. We left them to it!

Saturday was just round the corner. On Friday night we made a visit to the Safari Club, my mate Stilks was on the door, nice to be in the company of good people.

This place was the complete opposite of the Irish pub on Sunday. Pleasant people just wanting to enjoy themselves. We only had a couple and went back to be ready for the morning.

We arrived about 9.30. Wanting to remain impartial before the fight, we went to visit Wally and Phoebe Coates. Good friends for many years, me and Wally had done a lot together. I watched Leonard and Sam grow up from babies. Great family.

At 10am I noticed the Stocking (Smith) boys had arrived. Big Jimmy and little Wally, ex pro boxer.

I went to speak with Kenny and Mark to the Stockings. It was happening within 10 minutes.

It started off very slow, never really warming up. Kenny was playing defensive and Jimmy just taking lunges at him. Punches weren't really being landed by either side. Kenny was probably trying to wear Jimmy down, but to spoil his plan little Wally jumped up and took his place. It wasn't getting any better, a heavyweight fighting a lightweight. So then they switched back.

About this time, young Crockett came out of his Fathers trailer with a beautiful, white carved stock 12 bore and headed for Kenny.

Before he could pull the trigger, I grabbed hold of the barrel, lifting it above my head. He pulled it and it went off, right over my head.

I wrestled him for the big poppa and being the stronger, I took it quite easy, I then smashed it on the ground, pieces of the pretty carved wood all over the tarmac.

I never had a centre parting before!

Isle of Wight Festival 1970

It was the summer of 1970, everywhere uptown were posters advertising The Isle of Wight Festival, to be held in the last week of August. The bill was out of this world. Nearly all of the Underground bands were to be there, with a lot of artists coming from the States: Jimi Hendrix, The Doors, The Who, Jethro Tull, Sly and the Family Stone, Kris Kristofferson, Black Widow, Leonard Cohen, Donovan, a favourite of mine, Hawkwind, and many others.

I had a meeting in the back room at the Swan, Stockwell, with my friend Little Dickie from the flats there one day, and he introduced me to this young American fella called Chuck. The reason Dickie had bought him in was, the guy had thousands of acid tabs. Dickie had flooded the South London market with them and the guy still had thousands left. The tab of the day was Californian Sunshine, a very strong orange coloured one. Apparently this was the sister, Californian Cream, cream being the colour.

"They come highly recommended, mate." Said Dickie. Coming from him, that was enough. We had first become friends '64, in the Mod years. We discussed the prices and Chuck, being so nervous about still holding so many, made a deal better than I would have ever tried for. Hunky-dory! I now had summit to go to work with at the IOW Festival. It was getting close now and I was rebuilding the rear seat of my Volks Beetle to hold the contraband. The festival started on Wednesday 26th but decided to get there early and duck the radar.

I arrived at the ferry on the Sunday and applied for a ticket. Apparently, according to their book, the Volks was 3" too long to get in the medium size pricing range. I went to my tool kit an' took out a club hammer and smashed the protruding tail pipe about 5/6 inches into the exhaust box. I thought that was sorted, but no these guys obviously didn't like working Sundays and were taking it out on me. I argued the toss until they eventually got a tape measure out and physically measured the car, but taking in the contours of the car. This actually made the car longer not shorter. As the argument ensued, the queue for ferry was getting longer. Now other drivers were getting involved as well, until in the end they gave in. If they hadn't, either the ferry would leave almost empty or it would be late. I was to feel more of this kind of treatment on the island, we were obviously not wanted by the locals. Even shopping for essentials in the towns on route for the site, the feeling was there. Eventually over 600,000 people arrived and it was, according to the Guinness book of Records, the largest festival ever in the World. It's surprising the island didn't sink, that's over six times the population of the island at that time.

Following the temporary signs attached to the lamp posts, I found my way to the other side of the island, the venue. Here was a massive car parking and camping area. I kept going until I was at the extreme end. Here were some other early hippies and they had found some bales of hay in the field adjacent. They were passing them over the fence and building themselves little huts, I joined in. I soon had a one bed ground floor studio flat of my own!

I soon hitched up with a Daily Mirror page 3 girl. We spent days tripping and shagging in my new gaff.

When we eventually ventured out into the daylight, we were amazed at how fast the big field was filling up. I wanted to work but I had never really sold without introductions, so I had to learn how to hustle in a crowd.

"Hello mate, have you got any acid?"

"No, sorry."

"Would you like some?"

This is how I spent most of Friday. By this time the gaff was packed with long hairs, all looking for drugs. They were even asking me if I needed hash! Passing the entrance to the back stage, I saw little Roger Daltrey of The Who. We had crossed tracks a few times but weren't good friends or anything. In fact we didn't even get on.

"Oy geez!" He addressed me.

"Yes Rodger, how's it going?" Always respectful.

"Do you know anybody who's got tabs?"

"Yes, me!"

"You bes' come wiv me."

I followed him to the gate. "Passes please." Said security

"Here's mine an' his is in the tent waiting for him."

"Make sure he carries it, else he can't come in."

Roger said nothing, just stared at the jobsworth.

Inside the tent, I showed my wares. They seemed impressed.

"What else can you get?"

"Anything you want."

"Right you're here wiv us!"

I was happy here back stage, doing their shopping for them.

It was Saturday morning and their mooeys were like camel's cunts. They needed summit to wet their whistles with. It was decided that they wanted a case of melons. Not summit I'm gonna get on site, no matter what I would pay. So they loaded me up with money and sent me to find a cab and go to town. Whilst on this somewhat awkward task, I met a journalist who wanted to interview me. So I said yes, you need to take me to the shop and I will answer all your questions on return. He agreed, so I've now got the cab fares, as part of my regular sales income. Happy daze!

Returning to the tent, I took my fisherman's knife from its sheaf and started slicing the melons. The knife was one I captured whilst working on the fishing boats of Cornwall in the late '60s. It was an impressive looking Victorinox with a bright yellow handle. The day was getting on and their turn on stage was later that night. Whilst I was on the way to go shopping for the melons, I had nicked a road sign, I had ideas. I also bought a small black paint and a small white one, alongside a small paint brush. Back at the tent, after I had catered for the band, I took out the road sign. I painted white over the 'No Waiting' and with the black wrote a simple 'ACID'. I then attached it to a broom handle. With this I went right in the middle of half a million ravers and sat down, sign in hand. "What the Hell the police can do?" As the reggae song goes. Are they gonna send in enough cops to combat half a million acid heads! There was a constant queue, all day. I was loving it. The Who came on for a whole hour and were nothing like I remembered them from Mod days. They stole the show, even doing Pinball Wizard from Tommy. Pete Townsend had come a long way. I was so proud, these were London boys of 'My Generation', which they also played. When they came off stage I rushed back to join them. Using the pass Rodger gave me, I went back stage. Pete Townsend wanted drinks. Taking orders, I went out into the festival and bought what they wanted. I used the coins that I had taken from the tabs earlier, also offering my change to the stall holders. The notes were accumulating in my pockets!

I had one more day to do go, no time to relax for long in my haybale house now, I needed to graft whilst I could. My page 3 girl, obviously bored that I was working and not paying her any attention, had disappeared. Sorry girl, pennies first, pussy second!

The Who, now having done their shift, were free to go, but like a lot of other artists, were enjoying the festival. Sunday was promising to be a good night, with Jimi Hendrix on about midnight. It started with Ian Anderson of Jethro Tull doing a solo on his flute. The audience by now were completely out of their heads on acid. The sound of it was touching the finer parts of their brains. Only acid could do that! I was back out in the audience with my road sign at the time, still selling quite well. I stuck it out for the entire Jethro Tull performance. When Leonard Cohen came on a few people were leaving, so with trade slowing, I decided to go back stage.

The Who had obviously rested a while and were back up in time for Jimi Hendrix. He was the one everyone wanted to see. They wanted a case of water, so I went shopping again. Everything I bought always had a profit margin for me, they understood that and I was happy.

They didn't want any more drugs that night, they had probably reached tilt, like thousands of people here, you can only keep it up for so many days. Besides many had to get back to work on Monday!

The night started of a bit folky with Donovan and Ralph McTell, finally coming to life with Free. They finished after midnight and within minutes we were being entertained with the tune that Hendrix finished Woodstock with. Star Spangled Banner, the American national anthem. It must have been the best moment for the Americans in Woodstock, to hear your national anthem by Jimi Hendrix.

The Who were all sat outside at their table, a spliff was going round and they had the munchies.

"Any melons left?" I was asked by Rodger.

"Yer, I get them for you." I said and retrieved them.

There was about half a case left. I got my knife out and started to slice them at the same time as Jimi started singing 'Foxy Lady', a favourite of mine. I stopped a minute to hear the first guitar riff, brilliant. I continued to slice the Alicante melons, as the band were taking them to their dry mooeys. Everybody was happy.

Then this hippie bird with lots of curly ginger hair came across to me.

"Can I borrow yer knife?"

"Jus' wait whilst I finish cutting these melons an' ya welcome.

I had now done what I had to and passed her the big blade.

Much to my surprise, she mounted the stage, with it in her german band, heading straight for Jimi. As she raised it to stab him in the back, two security guards stopped her, fair does to the security men, they were on the ball. They probably saved his life. I never saw my knife again.

He died a few weeks later in Notting Hill, he suffocated on his own puke age 27. A waste of one of the best musicians ever.

The Ville

It was the Easter of the Brixton riots, 1981. I missed it all, as I was serving twenty eight days in HMP Pentonville. This is what happened.

I had just got a large consignment of weed arrive, it was enough to flood the Brixton area easily and there was a lot more to get rid of, on top.

My mate Ginger had some connections north of the river. Even though I didn't normally cross the river, this was in Highbury, a long way from the dreaded East End.

Because we were crossing, we decided that it would be safer to take a train from Brixton to Highbury. It wasn't a million miles from the station to where we had to go, so being fit young fellas we decided to walk. Ging decided to carry the sample and keep a few yards behind me. We often done this, so if one was to be apprehended, the other could just walk away.

I was on a zebra crossing, when this NSU Ro80 drove very fast across it, almost hitting me.

I screamed, "Bastard!"

The car reversed back up and two young Jamaicans got out. They ran towards me shouting, "Who you calling a bastard?" I had to act quickly, beside me on the pavement was a galvanized bin with a swing handle. I grabbed it and took the first one out easily. Now I was chasing the other one, just as I caught him and started to punish him, a load a cops in shirt sleeves and no hats appeared and saved him from further damage. I was arrested and taken into the Police station. Now, the strange thing was this all happened by the back gates of Highbury Police station, that's why they had no jackets or hats.

Back in the cop shop, I was banged up whilst the two young Jamaicans were being interviewed. When they were ready they took me to the charging desk. There they agreed that I couldn't be charged with assault, as the two had admitted that they took it to me, but I was to be charged on the relatively new charge of racial abuse.

"Racial fckn' what?" I shouted at them.

"Well you called them black bastards."

"I didn't know their colour or how many there was, I just shouted 'Bastard'"

"It's a case of two peoples words against one. We have to take the evidence from two people before just one."

"That's bollocks!" I screamed. "I have been bought up in the Jamaican community of Brixton, also I have lived and worked on the island of Jamaica, can I be a racist?"

Nobody wanted to listen and I was charged accordingly. When they wanted my name and address, I gave them a wrong'un, now they wanted my dabs, my fingerprints, so I refused.

They can't take someone's dabs by force without a Magistrates Order. So now I was waiting to go up in court on a racist charge in the wrong name. With the criminal record I had, I was liable to get a lot more punishment in my real name, so a wrong'un was necessary.

I stepped into the dock to answer to the charge. The first thing the cops said was they wanted an order to take my dabs by force. He said yes once I'd been weighed off. Well that was on my side, as he wouldn't know my real name until I was weighed off. Hunky-dory!

I was shocked when he gave me twenty eight days, as an unknown person, ie no previous record. I was taken down to the cells below to await transport to my new home. Then the cops took me out again and took my dabs, it was no use objecting, they had a Magistrates Order, that meant any amount of violence was allowed to get them. I went easily.

I'd already guessed it would be The Ville, as that's where you go for three months or less. I had twenty eight days, and in them days you served half so I'd worked out I was due out on Good Friday.

Pentonville is a shithole of a prison. Full of paraffins, tramps who commit petty crimes to get somewhere warm to live.

I had not been long out of hospital with a broken back, the last thing I needed now was to have to climb up all them steel stairs to my cell, so when I had a medical I told the Doctor. He made it so I was to be on the 'ones', a place I knew from my past was the best place to be, but what I didn't realise was the 'ones' here was where they housed all the worse conditioned paraffins and it was two to a cell.

I was moved into this peter with the smelliest paraffin you could imagine. I banged the door to no avail. In the morning I spoke to the landing officer and begged him to move me, I said if I was refused, I would put the para in hospital, just to get rid of him. They took notice and I was put into a single cell on the 'ones'.

I only had fourteen days to serve, or so I thought. I used to get two hours association every night, where I could watch TV. I wasn't into TV as such but liked to watch the news, especially my last week there, as it was all going off in Brixton, the riots had started. It seemed they were going to peak at that weekend, being the Easter weekend.

I was due out on Good Friday at 6am, well I was up packed and ready by 3am! My door didn't open until breakfast time and I rushed straight into the office.

"Nobody has come to me for my release!" I blurted.

"We don't do releases on Weekends or Bank Holidays."

"So I'm not being released 'til Monday?"

"Monday is a Bank Holiday as well. Your EDR is now Tuesday."

"So I have to serve four days extra?"

"I'm afraid so."

What could I say?

I was released on the Tuesday after Easter under my real name!

By the time I got back to Brixton, the only activity left was a bit of smoke rising off the burnt out buildings. It had gone very quiet, summit Brixton never was.

Herbie's Haversack

A mate of mine, Jihadi John, as we call him, is an Iraqi and definitely looks the part. We had both had a couple of liveners outside Regina's bar one day, and I was having a nice time with him and Frank, but now it was time for us all to go home. As John stood up to go, he pulled on a heavy looking rucksack and walked off through the square. I roared with laughter, he turned round, wondering what the fuck I was laughing at. "Sorry John but an Arab shouldn't walk around wiv a rucksack on his back." I shouted, an' everybody joined in with the laughter.

This reminded me of a crazy adventure during the late '70s. After a spat of IRA bombings in London, people were becoming extremely suspicious of unaccompanied bags of any sort.

I was sat indoors one morning when the phone went, it was an old friend of mine from Herefordshire, Herbie. He was a country boy, who played the small Welsh version of bagpipes, called reed pipes, very well. In fact, when Mike Oldfield, recorded the twenty five minute track 'Tubular Bells' in the mid '70s, he was asked to do some backing music for the main track.

" 'Allo mate, what you up to?"

"Jus' got back from India, I have summit to show you. Can you pick me up from Brixton tube?"

"When?"

"I've to get from Heathrow yet, I'll phone you back when I know."

"Hunky-dory!"

About half an hour later. "I'm due in Brixton in 25 mins."

"I'll wait outside in the street."

He appeared on the pavement, long curly black hair and a wild beard, he looked like he belonged to an ancient Celtic time. He jumped in the motor, throwing his rucksack onto the back seat, putting him arms around me. We were good friends years ago and it was good to see each other again.

"F'ckn' 'Ell mate, I'm glad to be back now. India is OK but its such a hassle, if you're white! It's OK for you townies but I'm a country boy and not use to it. Anyway, you wait 'til you try this bit a hash I bought back, you'll sell it easy. Come on, take me for a pint mate, I've had a thirsty day."

I pulled off Brixton Road into Acre Lane and at the first bus stop, I pulled over to make room for the passing traffic.

"Herbie, excuse the pun, stop beating around the bush an' give me a taster before we get to the boozer!"

He reached across to the back seat and retracted a not very pretty rucksack, it has obviously seen some of the rougher parts of India. After a bit of fumbling about he produced a banana. As he peeled back the skin, it exposed a chunk of black hash the shape of a banana. I'd never seen anything like that before.

"That's a good disguise Herbie!" I said jokingly, as really it wouldn't have fooled anyone.

"No mate that's the way it comes, Malawi style!"

Even though I had never smoked, I was always happy to chew on a sample of summit new. He passed me the whole banana and I foolishly bit off a big chunk. We then went down the road to a Young's pub, The Hope & Anchor to quench our thirsts.

Once we had two pints of Guinness in front of us, only then could we chat about India in general and of course, Malawi and the price of bananas. Before I had even finished my first pint, I felt a distinct coldness and a very dry mouth. It wasn't like any hash I had eaten before, it was a very strange combination of hot and cold feelings at the same time, and boy wasn't I thirsty! We sat there knocking back the Nigerian Lager, as Herbie called it, until the last bell went. Where had the morning gone?

Herbie had obviously been chewing on a banana earlier as his mince pies were bright red, as mine probably were also, if only I could see them. I definitely wasn't getting a very clear vision out of them! We were both completely fuckfaced and I had to drive home yet! We must have looked a mess as we attempted to steer our unsteady bodies towards the door.

I don't think I got out of second gear, for fear of mounting the curb and killing some innocent bystander. We eventually made it back to my pad and collapsed into the big sofa. I turned to look at Herbie, as he was clearly trying to say summit.

"Where's my rucksack?"

"Don't tell me you left it in the boozer! Go check the car."

Herbie returned empty handed.

"Charlie we need to go back to the pub and get my bag."

"But Herbie it will be shut now!"

"But it full of Malawi bananas!"

"I ain't driving no more mate. We'll have to phone a sherbet dab."

Twenty minutes later we were pouring ourselves into to an unsuspecting taxi.

"Hope 'n' Anchor, Acre Lane, driver."

We arrived to, as suspected, a totally shut pub. We rang the doorbell to no avail, well what publican answers his door bell at 3:30 in the afternoon? So we needed a plan.

The state of us two, it would have taken a plan to open a can of cornbeef. We had to think of summit soon, we had a taxi driver waiting outside the pub for us. Also outside was a Military vehicle of some sort that wasn't there earlier. We were too out of it to even contemplate why a squadie truck was parked outside a battle cruiser in Brixton.

Staring at the ground in desperation, I noticed the beer hatch in the pavement. These could be secured from the inside but in these days nobody bothered, the dreyman could deliver the kegs whilst the barman went about his duties upstairs.

"Herbie, take a side of the beer hatch mate."

The hatch came up no problem, god knows what the cabbie was thinking, apart from the fact he hadn't been paid yet. We dropped into the beer cellar and back up the wooden stairs into the bar.

In the bar, we soon got our bearings, even though we were still in a bad way, but no rucksack to be seen! Not knowing what to do next, we both collapsed into an old settee in the bar looking out into the garden.

There were a lot a people milling about at the bottom of the garden, so we decided to take the only option left, to open the French windows and join the crowd outside.

"Has anyone seen the rucksack I left here earlier?" Shouted Herbie. They all turned round and stared at us, including the Army Bomb Disposal Squad.

One of the Squaddies picked up Herbie's dirty little rucksack between two fingers an asked him if it was his. Herbie nodded. "We were just about to detonate it." Said a Bomb Squad member.

"Sorry about that." said Herbie, grabbing the bag and fleeing the garden with his bag. I was already unbolting the pub doors and we left there swiftly, straight into the taxi and home.

That was some serious shit, no hash had ever left me as out of control as this before. When we got home, Herbie rolled another spliff, I wasn't eating any more of that Malawi shit. I took up a banana and had a butcher's. It was wrapped in a real banana skin, with long thin dried grass, holding it all together. I asked Herbie about the little white dots, I could see now under closer inspection.

"It's jus' opium man!"

What a crazy day!

It sold fast and for good money, plenty of South London hippies liked summit different. Herbie collected his pennies and returned to his little cottage near Offa's Dyke on the Hereford-Welsh border. That was the only Malawi I had ever handled, it wasn't really my kinda thing.

I had always avoided all forms of opiates, seeing so many heroin addicts dying in these parts, I wanted no part of it. In fact I become fiercely very anti in the end. Not having any dealings at all with Junkies.

England, Scotland & Ireland

One winter's day in early '86, I went into Gossips Wine bar, in Gipsy road, West Norwood. I was dressed to the nines, as I was going to meet a Dulwich girl, for a posh night out.

I went up to the jump and ordered a glass a wine, from the Guv'nor, Eric. "You're looking swank tonight Charlie!" he said.

"Yes, I'm out wiv a bit a posh tonight."

My voice had attracted the attention of an afternoon wine barfly, a flashy dresser, in a blue blazer, cravat and blonde streaks in his hair.

He staggered over to me and started hanging round my neck, summit I really didn't like. I'd suffered from neck pains many years, since falling off of the back of a lorry.

"Graham, can you please leave me alone?"

All he did was to stare me in the face, not loosening his grip on me at all.

"Graham get ya f'ck'n arms off me." I said, lightly pushing him away. "Now leave me alone!"

He staggered back and shouted at me. "So you fink ya hard do you Charlie Breaker?"

He went to the door, opened it and shouted. "Come on then hard man, come fight me!"

I didn't want this, so I tried to ignore him but he was calling me all sorts of insulting things.

My rep could get damaged here tonight, I thought, I'll just give him a quick lesson.

I stepped outside to face him and he pulled out a shiv, well that was it, I wasn't risking getting a mars bar down me boat race. I beat him mercilessly, leaving him in a pool a blood on the floor. I really had seen red. What was I gonna do? I hadn't long been discharged from HMP Brixton, surely I would get a recall. Not summit I wanted, things were just picking up for me. I had to do a runner.

I walked as fast as I could to get away from the scene. I only lived round the corner. I went in and grabbed a handful of cash, an ounce of coke I had bought earlier, loaded a few bits into the back of my new Mercedes Estate and hit the road. I hadn't a clue where I was going.

I got on the M25 and headed north. I suddenly thought about my friends Tony Devine and Tommy Castle from Blackpool, who were due down soon to score. I could kill two birds with one stone, it would get me out of the area and I could get rid of the coke at the same time.

I stopped at a motorway services for a coffee and a map. The coffee to keep me awake, and the map because I'd never been more North East than Brum. It was much the same roads, the M1 and the M6. The maps made it about 250 miles. If I caned it on the motorways, I could be in Blackpool before the pubs shut.

Now which pub was I gonna start at? I got lucky, because Tommy was very well known locally, I was in the right pub within minutes of reaching town but he wasn't. A friend of his escorted me to his terraced house.

It was my first time up a North West back street. In London, our terraces run back to back, so no back entrance. Here they had a front entrance and a back one, opening out onto a scruffy back street, this is where it all happened.

"Breaker what the f'ck ya doing here, pal?"

"Jus' get me off the street Tommy, is me Merc alright out there?"

It definitely looked a bit out a place amongst the old transit trucks an' run down cars. "The neighbours will soon know your wiv me."

I was ushered off the street into the kitchen and sampled North West hospitality. His wife was a good cook.

"If you wanna a bed for the night, can I show you upstairs, pal"

"I'd like to empty me car first, please Tommy."

"The boys will do that for you."

I went with the boys to carry my belongings in and get my ounce of gear. "I'll sort the money out for that in the morning," said Tommy, once he'd seen the shiny white crystals. He sent me to bed with a jug of cider, not that I needed a lot of help that night.

Downstairs in the morning, a fantastic breakfast was put in front of me, so nice I can taste it as I write.

It wouldn't be long before the Blackpool cops would be checking on the owner of a near new Merc parked in the back street Tommy told me, so decided to move on.

I decided to go to Ireland, to be well and truly out of the way there. Tommy's boy went and got me a ferry timetable for Stranraer from a local travel agent. On checking the ferry times and the time necessary to check in beforehand, it was decided that I would break the journey into two. Greta Chase Hotel was about half way. I said my farewells to this lovely family and I got on the road again.

Just before you leave the M6 to go for Stranraer was the lovely hotel, probably once the home of a rich family.

I went to the souvenir shop out of a matter of interest and ended up buying a joke Scottish passport. Once I had devoured a Scottish breakfast of Tattie scones, Haggis, flat sausage etc., I hit the road once again. It was about two hours on the A75 and there was a ferry in about four and a half hours.

On arrival at the port, the back of my car was thoroughly searched. I had forgot I had a little 9mm pistol under the spare wheel. I suspected the worse but they took it very much a matter a fact.

"We have a serious plague of rats in London at the moment," I tried to lie as nicely as possible.

"Yes, I heard that." The one said. These guys were Irish and probably worked for the ferry.

"I'm very sorry Sir, but I can't let it on the ferry. There's a Redstar office here in the terminal, I'll show you where it is."

He jumped into the passenger seat and we drove to the office. I was racking my brain as to who would want a pistol arriving on their doorstep in London.

At the Redstar office, they were equally as obliging. Offering to disguise the pistol for me. "Well, we wouldn't anybody knowing what's in the parcel, would we now."

Eventually I thought of an address, with it being so well disguised, I paid and we went back to the ferry queue. He chatted all the way and bid me a safe journey. A bit different to Brixton Old Bill.

The ferry pulled into the old Larne docks and we disembarked on to the pontoon. Safe at last I thought.

I thought too soon, as we went round the first bend, we were faced with the UK Army, a big automatic was mounted in the back of a Landrover and rifles were being pointed in my direction, I opened my window as directed.

"Passport!"

It was about to come on top. These guys were checking for people running away from the UK, like me. I had to think fast. Pulling out my dodgy Scottish passport from The Gretna Chase Hotel was all I could think of to bide time. I passed it to the soldier, who burst into laughter, calling his friend over to see it. They both found it very funny. He handed it back and waved me on. Phew! A narrow escape there. It was my lucky day.

I didn't feel like much driving now, so asked the locals where to go, to get my head down. I was pointed to a boarding house.

I walked through the front door to find just a table, with a big book. A man appeared from nowhere an after I gave him £15, he gave me a key with a wooden tag on it and the number 13. Lucky for some I thought. He pointed to the bare wooden stairs and I ventured to find my room. It was literally one single bed and a beside table, boasting a copy of the Holy Bible.

I decided it was time to try the local Guinness. As I went downstairs, the same man reappeared.

"Could you point me to the nearest pub please?"

The man just opened a door in the hallway to expose a room full of men all drinking, and mostly all on Guinness at that.

I was to experience the best pint I'd ever had. To me the mention of Larne, makes me think of Guinness.

As the night went on, more and more men were arriving and the strange thing was that the eighty or ninety men in there all had wooden key rings! There's no way there's that many rooms here, probably twenty at the most. A key meant you were resident, so you could drink here all night!

I was sad to leave the lovely people of Larne, down to earth Paddys.

The next stop was Ballycastle, also in Antrim. I found a brilliant B&B for £20 a day and as much as I could eat. The first morning I asked the landlady for a taxi to take me to a pub, she called her husband.

"No extra charge, it's all included in the B&B price." I was learning to love Ireland.

He dropped me off at the Diamond bar, in the square. I was greeted with much gusto by the Guv'nor. This was to be my local. I gelled that day wth a big truck driver called Horse, we became good pals. If there was ever a party in Ballycastle, we were there.

One day he said we could go see a Shelali band in William McCarroll's, as this other bar was called.

At 11pm, as the Diamond bar was shutting, a crowd of us went to McCarroll's, it was filling up fast and the band were tuning their instruments. When the fiddle player finished doing his solo, the band started.

I had never heard such a band in my life, not sad, not romantic, not lyrical, just good fun music.

After the band had played for about two hours, they sat down to have a beer. I thought it was the end to the evening, until the staff bought out massive trays full of sandwiches and crisps! After a break they went back on for a while and it all finished about 4am.

As I was chatting to Horse, a customer came over an asked if we wanted to go back to his place. Horse volunteered for both of us before I could have a say.

Then an amazing thing happened, the same man

phoned his wife, this is 4am!

"Can you get Colleen out a bed an' tell her to put some pies in the oven an' make some sandwiches, I got a bunch a chaps coming over."

Can you imagine, back in London, a man phoning his wife at 4am with instructions like that, these days?

London in the '80s, the women were already heavily influenced by Simone de Beauvoir, The Cosmopolitan Magazine, Female Equality, Burn the Bra brigade, etc. Many old school husbands had already split with their wives over it.

Anyway, back to Ballycastle, several cars were loaded with half pissed men and transported to a house on the outskirts of town. We all staggered up the garden path and through into a large lounge.

As we were being treated to all kinds of spirits, in came a shiny tea trolley, creaking under the weight of the food, being pushed by a girl of about 14 years old. We never saw her again.

We were invited to help ourselves and we did. As we were stuffing our faces with steak pies or beef sandwiches, the host was shouting out for his wife.

A pretty girl in her early thirties walked in the room. He then picked up a large tambourine looking drum and started hitting it with a short stick. I was to find out later it was called a Bodhrán.

As the music got faster, his wife was instructed to do an Irish dance in the middle of the floor to entertain us! I just took it all in with amazement.

Whilst they were all having a break later, I asked Horse why the Guinness badge on the Bodhrán was in red.

"The red harp signifies the RUC, The Royal Ulster Constabulary, not Guinness."

"You mean he's a policeman?"

"Yes an' this is where he lives, it's a Police Station as well. Do you want to see the cells?"

"Not really." I was sobering up fast, the last place I wanted to be was in a Police Station!

"They are effectively, British cops. You are safe here."

Little did he know. I wanted to go back to my B&B now! Horse arranged a lift and I was gone.

India, Kent & Turkey

A fellow I knew, Frankie, had robbed a lorry full of new tyres on the way to the main distributors. Car tyres were a very lucrative business and could be easily sold from the hundreds of small tyre shops around South London. I was into buying the loads and distributing them myself throughout my area.

But this time he came unstuck, they were bike and motorbike tyres of all sizes. The only places I knew that sold them were the bike shops. These were all monopolized by a couple of big companies, the largest was in South London, Pride & Clarke, and had a massive control over these. These guys didn't buy anything bent. He was stuck with thousands of tyres.

During WW2 the UK army in India used the Royal Enfield 350, known as The Bullet. The Army was equipped with mostly rifles and pistols made by who? Royal Enfield. Hence, The Bullet.

After the war there were hundreds left behind and they became very popular with the Indians. So a small company there bought the old tooling from Royal Enfield UK and opened Royal Enfield India.

Whilst I was visiting India one time, I decided to look up an old pal of mine, Brian, who had settled in Goa. He had set up a business there retailing these bikes and their parts. He had told me the Indian made tyres weren't fit for the bad roads, and getting good name tyres into the country was costing a fortune.

A bell rang in my head...

The next day I phoned Brian and asked exactly what sizes would fit the Bullet, and what he would be able to pay. I wrote them down and arranged a meet with Frankie. He had a slaughter full of bikes tyres that weren't going anywhere, so it was easy to come to a good deal for the 100s of tyres the sizes that Brian wanted. I got a 20 foot container delivered to my yard and Frankie with my boys loaded them ready for export.

The next day I phoned Brian, he was over the moon. But when I told him how many, he was taken back.

"Great I know, but I don't have that much money ready mate!"

"No probs, how long would you need Bri?"

"About 3 weeks mate!"

"I tell you what, I wanna come back out in about 6 weeks, allowing for delivery, that's about a month you have, is that ok?"

"Sure is, thanks mate!"

"I'm off to buy a secure container lock tomorrow an I'll post you a key."

"I can't wait, this will change my life."

Well, it wasn't gonna change my life, but would pay for my trip to India. I wanted to spend some time in Goa this time, I was always just rushing through.

I had booked a decent hotel on Baga beach and was looking forward to the break.

Goa was completely different to most of the other parts of India. It was originally a Portuguese enclave, they ran it for hundreds of years, until the Indians took it back in the '60s. So it was like a little bit of Europe in India. With its beautiful sandy beaches, it became a great place to live, especially for the hippies an other sub cultures that enjoyed Indian marijuana!

I was recommended a driver for £5 a day, including

fuel, to escort me about the many diversities of Goa. Kabir would sleep outside the hotel in his Standard 10, when I turned in for the day. I wasn't much into hotel food, so Kabir would take me to all the little food huts owned by his Hindu friends. One such day was Holi Day and the Hindi temples were emptying out into the local food huts, where they continued to party. We were in one such place and the only other Western person there was a girl called Caroline, from Canterbury in Kent and her husband Mustafa, a Turk, on their honeymoon. I got on well with them and taking their details, promised to visit them after we had all returned back to the UK.

On return to work, a little Turkish firm were wanting lots of engines, gearboxes and back axles from the latest Transit out, the Mk 5. These hadn't been out long, so there was only one way to keep them happy, send out the boys. I would buy the full strips but didn't want the shells in my yard. Half a dozen times a week, a small truck would turn up, the load sheeted, to be unladen in my yard. So, once deposits were made we would spray them black and crate them ready for the overland trip back to Turkey. Once there, their old MK 2 transits would be refurbished with MK 5 parts. It was a good business for everyone except the insurance companies, well they liked robbing people, so we got revenge!

These Turkish trucks were leaving almost every two weeks but suddenly they stopped coming and I didn't know why. It was about this time that I got a phone call from Caroline in Canterbury. Mustafa had landed a job running a motel on the southern coast of Turkey and they were moving over. So I asked to speak to him.

"Hi Mustafa, sorry I haven't been down, works been busy."

"Nothing wrong with that. As Caroline has told you we're moving to Turkey in a couple a weeks."

"What part?" Not that I knew it well!

"Ölüdeniz."

"Anywhere near Fethiye?"

"Yes actually, it's the nearest big town to there. Why, you know someone there?"

"As it happens I do an' I wanna go see them soon as I get time."

"Great, you can stay in my motel, I'm the manager."

"I'll def take you up on that. Lets keep in touch."

All I knew was that the transit parts buyers had a shop in Fethiye, I had no other details and now I had a native speaking guide! I could go see what the problem was. If I was being undercut, I could adjust my prices, there was plenty of leeway.

A month later I was landing in Dalaman airport, finding myself a 40 year old Merc Taxi, but the bonus was the driver spoke English. Climbing the mountains between the airport and Ölüdeniz, the driver said it's only about 50 miles but it would take us the best part of an hour and a half to get there.

The last bit of the journey was downhill between two forests, it was truly one of the most beautiful scenes I'd ever seen. Strangely, it resembled going down to a woman's crotch, with their forests either side.

Ahead, all we could see was the sea and then slowly the single floored buildings came into sight. No towers here, not even two floors were allowed.

Once there, I was greeted by Mustafa and Caroline, great people. They made me comfortable from day one, it couldn't be better.

The first thing after breakfast, I wanted to find the parts shop and get work out of the way, they had so many plans for me. We soon found the shop. They were gutted, because no second hand engines were allowed to be imported, they were declaring them as new.

Now the government was asking for receipts from Ford, being that it wasn't possible, they had to stop importing.

This little town of Ölüdeniz had only a few bars and restaurants, so we visited them all. They were great people, and I started enjoying real Turkish food, not just Donna Kebab, as was becoming the rage in London. Even the salads were full of flavour, the feta and olive being a favourite, and of course the King of Turkish salads, calf brain salad. Talking of food reminds me of a day out on a boat with Mustafa.

Mustafa had borrowed a small dinghy with an outboard motor, to take our little party to an island out at sea. It was the place where fishermen stopped to eat lunch and drink some local wine.

When we got there, we couldn't see anybody until we banged against the rickety pontoon, then a man came out to welcome us. I didn't fancy the pontoon at all, it was shaking under the weight of a six stone person an I was well over twenty. Well, the water was shallow so the worse was I would get wet.

We were escorted to a seating area in front of an old brick barbecue and Mustafa was finding what we wanted to eat. The boss here, or Chief as they say in Turkey, had taken some meat off the charcoals and he offered it around.

"What is it Mustafa?"

"I don't know how to say it in English."

I chewed on a bit but no one else was interested, they were shouting for chicken. Minutes later I could hear the sound of chickens, saying their last goodbyes to life on the island.

I was enjoying the raw red wine out of the barrel but decided I was gonna have to stop, if I was to survive another walk on the pontoon.

I managed to get the Chief to escort me and Mustafa around the little island. After we had walked about 500 yards, I saw a heap of porcupine quills on the side of the track.

"Is it alright if I get them, they're good for fishing floats?"

"Yes of course," Mustafa cut in, "they're off the animal you was eating earlier. It's called a porcupine mate!"

National Federation of Demolition Contractors Beano

Whilst living in woodland Kent, a fellow Londoner, Golden Ray, came down and built a new bungalow complete with an indoor swimming pool not far from me.

Ray Styles became a close friend and drinking partner. We drank regularly in the Vigo Inn on Wrotham road, The Villager in Vigo village or the Amazon in Harvel. All busy country pubs.

Ray ran a demolition company in Charlton, he had done well for himself, was always great company and a very great teller of jokes.

As a member of the NFDC he would always invite me to the many beanos. They were great fun, a load of wealthy men without any airs and graces, always ready for a wild pissup.

Sometimes we would go to the races and end up in a top restaurant nearby or at one of Barry Cope's famous racecourse seafood stalls. He had the best available, from wobbly wheels, to fresh whelks, dressed crab and lobster claws. We'd spend fortunes there, washing it down mugs of champagne. This is how these guys lived and I loved it.

Another common venue would be a five star hotel somewhere. The hotel would be sponsored by a big plant manufacturer, hoping the NFDC boys would be spending lots of money with them.

One such event was at a little seaside resort, Brixham. It was a nice hotel, obviously a stately home once, but it was very quiet, not really what the boys wanted. Hence we would go into town regularly and go to one of the many quayside ale houses. Liking the way the money was flowing, we would be offered lock-ins wherever we went, complete with big trays of sandwiches.

One day, by way of a change, we chartered a boat to take us out to sea. Straight after breakfast, we went down to the quayside and became nautical gentleman, not summit that would last. We thought we would have the boat to ourselves, but there were half a dozen tourists already on board. No big thing we thought.

Going to sea is thirsty work, it must be the salt air, and the obvious happened, we hadn't been on board long before there were requests for some liquid refreshments. Apart from spirits, all they had on board was Elephant Ale at 7.2 proof or the local scrumpy at 7.5. A recipe for disaster.

A couple of the younger ones were getting louder by the bottle, and the louder they got, the more they swore. Mr & Mrs Average Holidaymakers were not enjoying it at all but the young fellas couldn't see it.

When one of the fellas went to refurbish the ale supply, he spotted a Mr Average complaining to the Captain, demanding that the vessel should about turn and return them to the quayside. The youngster rushed across and grabbed hold of the man by his collar and threatened to throw him in the briney, so he could swim back.

Then the Captain raised his voice and next thing you know, everybody is out on the deck, all shouting at each other. Not a pretty sight.

The Captain got out a loud howler and shouting over everyone, he demanded we all went back to the cabin, he was returning to the quay. Well that made it worse, we had paid for a day out and it wasn't happening. A few of the elder men got into an argument with him and he said he was about to radio the police, and even worse, the bar was shut. Ray, ever the diplomat, ushered us all back into the cabin and told us he would speak to the Captain on his own. When he come back, he had cracked a deal. No radio call to the cops. The youngsters, it was agreed, had reached tilt an didn't need any more anger fuel. Lastly, with the beer running out, the Captain was gonna serve the elders with gin & tonics etc., and to top it he would refund us.

Everybody seemed happy with the deal and it was decided to refuse the refund, they had ample funds to continue in a quayside boozer.

The young'uns were the first to disembark and disappeared up the harbour wall, whereas we went to the nearest watering hole.

Never a dull moment with the NFDC!

One day I went to The Vigo, I had to deliver a Saab 900 to a local fella, Nick Watnaugh, son of a Polish WW2 refugee. Once I had finished the deal with Nick, Ray captured me and whispered in my shell like, there was a hotel beano coming up, it was sponsored by a big American plant company, was I up for it? Not many Benny, I didn't need asking twice.

"It's at the Stoke Moat House Hotel."

"Where's that Ray?"

"Stoke on Trent." He said, faking a northern accent.

I thought Stoke on Trent was rhyming slang for

"bent", as in bent as a nine bob note. I didn't realise it was an actual place.

"Well you got a couple a weeks yet mate, gives you time to get a fancy dress together."

"Fancy dress?"

"Yes the yanks have organised a big prize fancy dress party on the second night."

"Big prize Ray?"

"Yes, the winners get big discounts on the plant they buy."

"Very clever, if I win, you can have the discount. No room for a concrete crusher on my car front!"

I was already planning my costume. I had not long come back from Casablanca, where I bought a djellaba gown, a fez red hat and some pointed toe sandals. I was gonna be Saddam Hussein.

On the day, we was in Brum within a couple of hours, and in another hour we were in Stoke.

The first night they had laid on a big meal, and even got the Stoke Mayoress out to sit on the top table with them. She gave a big speech about the hotel just opening today, to commemorate the birth of Ebenezer Wedgwood, the grandad of fine bone china.

The yanks must be expecting some big sales this weekend, they had proper laid it on bigtime. After the meal, we went to the bar to top up with all the free champagne and wine. There was a pool table as well, so it was a good atmosphere.

Until at midnight the barman announced that he was shutting the bar.

It was one of Tony's boys again, first to lose it.

"You're going nowhere, get your arse back behind that bar, or I'll run it!"

That's the way it remained for the weekend. The

barman wasn't allowed to go home.

The next day, Tony wanted to go get a Chinese in town but he was already pissed as a parrot.

"Charl, do us a favour, take me to town in me Roller an' we'll get a Chinese."

We jumped in his Rolls Royce, well I jumped, he fell in and we drove the mile or so into town.

Once there, we asked someone where the Chinese was. It was about 200 yards down the pedestrian precinct but we had to drive round the other side of town to get there.

"Fuck it Charl, we'll drive across the precinct."

50 yards into the precinct, there's a Mr Plod.

"Excuse me sir, this is a pedestrian precinct, you have to turn back."

"Fuck off you dirty copper!" Shouted Tony.

"I'm sure he doesn't mean that." I said.

"Yes I do, dirty copper! Come on let's drive Charl."

That's what I did before it escalated any more. Outside the Chinese, Tony said pull up, so I said get out, I'll park somewhere. No, park it here, it's my car, he said. So I did, but I craned my neck every five minutes and no one came. I thought they will be waiting around the corner when we leave, wrong again. This is a strange town.

Meanwhile, it had been discovered that there was a swimming pool directly below the bar. It was hugely popular with the young set. They were getting pissed and going down to the pool all night. One night, one had fallen asleep in a locked toilet and he was rescued by having the brand new door smashed off its hinges.

When the hotel staff realised the next day what had happened, they decided to lock the big glass doors at midnight. Can you guess what happened that night? Yes, the doors were demolished, professionally. No stopping these boys! Me and Ray went out for the last day, to have a look round and stop for a curry. I needed to straighten out a bit for the drive home in the morning.

Just inside the hotel doors, in the lobby, was a life size statue of Mr Wedgewood. As we got back we were shocked to see his head was now on the floor. These guys were definitely demolishers.

We had a couple of light ales and got our heads down for the night. In the morning, I noticed the tea service in the room was all Wedgewood. Well, I weren't leaving that behind and packed it in my wheelie bag. Strangely enough as we all waited outside to say goodbye, everybody's bags were clinking with the same bone china.

Ray told me later that month, that the hotel was shut down for four weeks, due to damage, before reopening.

Joe, The Archetypal Gangster

A brief history.

Joe Pyle was born North East London in 1937, just before WW2.

He never spoke much about his life as a kid, except he had a loving mother and had been a junior boxer.

After the war the family moved to Carshalton, from where he eventually turned pro. He had 6 fights in under four months and retired with a 4:2:0 record. I asked him once, why retire so soon?

"I didn't wanna spend the rest my life travelling around London on buses. All the time I spent training an boxin', I could have get meself a fair few bob. There was no money in boxing, only for the promoters."

Less than twenty years later he was co-promoting unlicensed boxing with Alex Steene. The most famous of their promotions being the notorious Shaw-McClean trio.

Joe was already having scrapes with the law, but managed to keep his liberty. Until one day in the Pen Club, Fleet Street, him and Johnny Nash went into room with the Manager of the club, and only two men came out. Joey and Johnny were arrested and put on remand. In those days you got hung for murder.

Joe told me an interesting story about his Mother visiting him in the clink.

"When she came in the visiting room, Charl, from the

look on her face, you would've thought she had a mouth full a wasps. Before she even sat down, she shouted at me."

"Joey, it's on the street, that their saying you will say Johnny done it an' walk free! Please tell me this ain't true."

"No, Mother it's not true, we have had an agreement, if I say I saw nuffin' an' he says the same, with no evidence there's no case against either of us an' we both walk."

"Me Mother sat down an' said..."

"Oh Joey boy I'm so glad, I'd rather see you swing than hear you walk out a grass!"

For me, that epitomizes life in London in the '50s. What an amazing person she was. I think a lot of her rubbed off onto him. He was a man of very strong principles.

One day we were all talking in the pub and this young fella came across to join us. He spoke about what a proper geezer I was. He told Joey about the time I served a three an 'arf stretch for a pal, rather than put him in the picture.

"What's special about that boy? He jus' done what we all should do, nuffin' special about that."

One of Joe's favourite sayings was... "A still tongue keeps a wise head, loose lips sink ships."

In the late '70s, I got heavily involved in supplying marijuana to the massive Jamaican market in Brixton. Not only were there thousands of Jamaican smokers, but it had become the thing to score from Brixton, as it wasn't very freely available elsewhere. Many streets in the area were lined with small time dealers, hanging about waiting for their regulars.

I didn't know until later that, when out on the town

one night with Mr Nice, Howard Marks, Howard was supplying Joey, who used a guy called Jim for distribution.

Jim was my link to the van loads that went into Brixton every week. I was positively the biggest weed dealer ever in Brixton because I was the only white guy that would deal with Jamaicans. My life then is depicted as Mr Breaker in 'Lock, Stock and Two Smoking Barrels'.

In the very late '90s, Joe set up some unlicensed shows with Freddy Batt, in Fred's club, Caesar's Palace, Streatham High Road. Once set up, Joe had passed the events over to his son Joe Jr., who co-promoted with Ricky English and his EBF titles to fight for.

I was running a small team of unlicensed boxers by now. My top trainer was a good boxer in his day, a Jamaican called Eric Wilson, a lovely man and brother to one of my best friends then, Leselve Wilson.

Then the calls started.

"Hello Charl, it's Joe, would you do me a favour, can you supply some boxers for little Joe at Streatham."

"Of course mate."

He was always in the background, using his influence to help little Joe.

The shows were selling out, plenty of bums on seats. If the boxer sold tickets, he shared the ticket money, so everyone was a winner.

At the top table on the stage was always Joe, me and Roy, accompanied by Joe's guests, whilst little Joe was the whip, and Ricky English the MC. It worked a treat.

Liam Galvin of Gangster Films recorded every one of the 'Pyle's Punchups'. A lot of these can be seen on YouTube or can be bought on Amazon.

We cut many a caper over the years, getting pictures in newspapers twice. I could quite easily turn this into a book, not a short story, so I must move on.

In 2005 Joe contracted motor neuron disease, a wasting away illness. I visited him many times, taking a few friends, a bottle of Brandy and a little bit a coke to kill his pain.

About a month before he died in 2007, he took a copper framed picture off the wall in his lounge and handed it to me. It was a photo of me, him and Jimmy White. Jimmy had given it to him as a birthday present, now Joe was giving it to me. I felt deeply honoured and will never part with it.

Joe's funeral was on a cold day, even showering us with hale stones as well as freezing rain, but thousands turned up. Probably the only turn out ever to compete with Gipsy King, Mark Ripley's.

I was asked to do a speech about Joe at the wake. It is on YouTube, Google 'Charlie Breaker Gangster' and it's the first up.

I said it was the end of an era. The Emperor was dead and the Empire will die as well. The underworld will split up and fight each other, dog eat dog. The unity would be no more, the Olden's weren't interested and the youngsters weren't capable. The power Joe held was gone forever.

As an example, as far as Joe was concerned we all had our areas, and therefore under his name control. To Joe I was Mr Brixton, so to speak. I would get a call from him.

"Hi Charl, you know Leroy Brown?"

"Of course Joe, he has a wine bar in Brixton."

"I knew you would, well he's been a bad boy, he owes Little Tony 30k and he is playing up."

"Leave it to me Joe, I'll sort it."

"Laters mate."

I would drive down to the wine bar and stroll in.

"Mr Breaker, welcome, get the champagne out girls!" All full of himself.

"I'll have a glass a bubbly in a minute, first we need to talk."

"Come to the back room. What's up Mr B?"

"Joey Pyle sent me here."

The worried looking fashion dread looks at me.

"What's up?"

"He says you owe Little Tony 30k, Tony wants you done but Joe said we'll sort it out."

"Of course, I'll get the dollar delivered to Joe in the morning. Can I have his number?"

"No but I will get him to phone you. Now all I need now is your business card an' a glass a champagne."

Passing me a card he said, "What's your fav bubbly?"

"Veuve Clicquot yellow label."

"Here's a bottle, enjoy at home, thank you."

That's the way things were sorted, no one dead, no one in prison. Joe had saved over 500 lives. The judges say we can't take the law into our own hands, but our way works, theirs don't.

A short tale to depict the power he had in the '70s.

I use to organise snatch backs, I use to get £60 - £100 a car depending on the circumstances.

One day I got a phone call from Lambeth North Central Finance, they were in Norwood that afternoon, could we meet. No probs.

They gave me half a dozen Brixton cars to snatch back and prices were agreed. Then they pulled out another snatch back authorisation paper.

"Do you mind doing a Peckham job?"

"I'm game for anywhere local."

"I can't get the Peckham boys to do it, we have gone right up to £600."

"Give it me, I'm scared of no cnt!"

He passed me the paperwork and I read it.

'Joseph Pyle, the Oglander Pub Peckham, a year old yellow S-type Jaguar.'

"Nobody can get that car, they'll get killed. I'll take this paperwork and you can scrub it off your list."

I took it to the pub and found Joey. I passed him the paperwork.

"Your gonna take my car are you?"

"Of course not Joe, jus' come to show you the paperwork. Nobody can touch your car."

"Thanks mate, what you drinking?"

We had a drink and a laugh about it, the official papers were now with Joey, no one could touch it.

Joe was cast in a platinum mould and it was thrown away after. There was no one like Joe.

1990 Benson & Hedges Masters

When I came out of HMP Brixton in '88, I went back to my country home. I was fortunate enough to own a timbered cottage, built on the cleared land of some ancient Kent forest. My front garden was an acre of meadowland, and to the rear was 5½ acres of dense woodland. It looked down onto the unmade country lane that I owned half a mile of. Whichever way you looked, you could see trees, it was a beautiful place to live.

A few things had changed in my absence, one was a new Governor in the village pub, The Amazon & Tiger.

Gary Greatwood was a big characterful and colourful man. When he wasn't working the rails taking bets at a racecourse somewhere, his big smiling face was beaming from behind the jump.

Not only did me and him gel very quickly but so did his son and my son, both 13 years old. His son spent many an afternoon at my place where I would take them into the pool room and show them how to play. I even had a bit cut off of the heavy end of two cues, to make them easier for the youngsters. They were really getting into it.

I spent many a day with Gary down at the rails with his price board an easel along with the massive leather bag that hung round his neck, guarding his tickets and money, and of course 'the book'.

Everyone knew Gary, including all the ticket touts,

and he could get a good ticket to any sporting event in the country.

One day, after returning from the Xmas break and back to work again at my car front on Keston Common, I slipped down the Amazon for a jar or two. Gary was there, beaming from behind the jump, a bit more full of himself than usual.

"Evenin' Gary, it looks like you had a good day on the rails today!"

"No mate, even better than that, come into the pool room I wanna show you summit."

I was waiting by the pool table when in he rushed, the big man's shirt flapping like a galleon under full sail. He then pulled out four tickets for the B&H Masters at the Wembley Conference Centre in February.

"Are they sold mate?"

"No way, these are front row seats for me, you an' the two boys."

"For real, front row!"

"Yes, you know me Charl!"

"I certainly do. What day does it fall on?"

"On a Saturday or Sunday in February mate."

"Wait till I tell Sam, he goes back to Bristol, to school, in two days but he can always come down at the weekends. He'll be over the moon Gazza. Thanks mate! How much are they?"

"This day is a treat on me, to thank you for all the help you given me over the Christmas period."

I went back to a stall up at the jump and swallowed a few pints of cider before going back home to tell my boy the good news.

"Dad, will it be on telly?"

"The B&H Masters final, of course but you'll be there to see it from the front row."

"No Dad, I want to tell all my friends to watch out for me."

Friday, after school, Sam jumped on a train to Meopham Station, where I picked him up and we proceeded to The Amazon & Tiger. The two boys soon disappeared round the back to the pool table. Not having customized cues here, they shared 'the short cue'. They were obviously very excited.

Swallowing the first pint greedily, I ordered two plates of sandwiches, one for the boys and one for the jump. It was a busy Friday night, the place was buzzing with the local travellers, a lot of whom had built on some land in Beechwood Drive, Culverstone. Some good ol' boys amongst them.

Gary was working on the rails on the Saturday, but we agreed to meet at the boozer on Sunday morning. I volunteered to drive, I couldn't let him treat us like this and let him drive as well.

Sunday morning, both suited & booted, Sam an I jumped into my big 560SEL Mercedes and headed for the pub. It wasn't open yet but Gary and I had a sneaky pint before we left for Wembley.

The 5600cc V8 greedily ate up the road and we were soon being ushered down to our front row seats. It was a bit early as yet, so we decided to go look at the snooker merchandise for sale on the first floor. I left there with a new Reilly cue, a pigskin cue case and a couple of gold chalk holders embossed with B&H. I treated the boys as well, Gary didn't want anything.

We then went back down to our bang smack in the middle, front row seats. The place was very noisy with thousands of punters looking for their seats.

Eventually it all went quiet as Mr Chamberlain, the ref, appeared.

John Parrot appeared closely followed by Stephen Hendry, the ref done his bits and John Parrot broke. The match was now underway.

There were a few good moments, but a lot of it lacked lustre. The boys seemed enthralled with it all, which was more important.

Lunchtime arrived not before time, we were all hank marvin. Gary then took us up to the restaurant on the top floor. He had obviously been there before, everyone knew him.

He ordered for us, he was like that, but it was always in great style if not a bit OTT!

He had coming a bottle of the top Rioja red wine and a bottle of 1961 Graham's Malvedos Vintage Port to get started. Wow, he knew his stuff.

Wine waiter now having done his job, the main waiter arrived and before he could say a thing, Gary started to order.

"Have you got pheasant on the menu today?"

"Yes sir."

"Well my friend Charlie will have two!"

I protested but to no avail. He was so happy to showing off, he was practically pouring the drinks down my throat. After we had done the wine with the first two courses, he ordered a big cheese board with which we had done half of this very expensive port.

"Waiter, we can't leave this excellent port, we need more cheese to finish it off!"

I had long reached tilt, my belt was digging into my hips but he wasn't giving up. As he was eating the last few grapes off the cheeseboard, he shouted summit to the flustered waiter and pulled out a Gold American Express card. I offered to club in but no, he waved me off, he was enjoying himself too much.

When the box came back with his gold card, as he retracted his card, I slipped a £20 tip inside.

Gary appeared so happy all time, especially when he was showing off. He reminded me a bit of the legendary '40s Laughing Policeman, with his big rosy cheeks.

I struggled to waddle down the many stairs to the ground floor and I finally collapsed into my seat. Parrot was doing a lot a boring safety shots and I nodded off.

Next thing I know is, my boy standing over me.

"Wake up dad, they've had to stop the game because of your snoring, dad, dad please!"

I opened by eyes an' focused on Mr Chamberlain looking very annoyed at me flanked by John Parrot, cue in one hand an' the other on his hip.

"Now, if we can resume the game ,Sir!" The ref shouted at me.

Sam took me away to the bar where I sat drinking coffee till the next frame.

"Dad, how embarrassing, I told all my friends to watch the match, I was so proud but not now!"

"Sorry Son." Was all I could say.

The Borstal Boy's Song

When I left Portland Borstal 55 years ago, I knew a song that was going round at the time, I've tried to recollect it. Correct me if I'm wrong please.

A Borstal Boy came home one day,
To find his girl had run away,
When he asked her why,
This is what she said..

'If you could live a normal life,
I would love to become your wife,
But you prefer a life of crime,
Well Borstal Boy go do yr time'.

One day in his cell,
The Borstal Boy rung his bell,
When the Screws arrived he was dead,
And the suicide note read...

'Dig mi grave deep,
And put roses by mi feet,
A dove on mi chest,
To show I died for love'.

You pretty girls keep in mind,
A Borstal Boy is hard ta find,
When ya find one, love him true,
'Cos a Borstal Boy will die for you.

Anybody else remember that song?

1994 Oliver McCall – Lewis

It was on the May 8th 1993, we were travelling with team Lennox to Vegas, my protégé Kevin Lueshing was going to USA for the first time, and Frank Maloney had asked me to come along to look after his mother as well. I had known Maureen Maloney many years, she was a neighbour of mine in South London, in fact her youngest, Eugene, went to the same Junior School as my boy Dyll.

It was to be the first time of many, going to Las Vegas, that was. It was very busy there, Don King had a full show of American boxers and Panix were taking some opposition. There were so many boxers I'd only ever seen on TV. Terry Norris was not on the bill but was there in the hotel reception when we arrived. On the bill was Julio Chávez, Héctor Camacho and Meldrick Taylor. Lennox was fighting Tony 'TNT' Tucker.

When we went down to the hotel lobby on the big day, Frank pulled me to one side to tell me he didn't have a whip! Would I help him? I agreed, even though I'd never done it before, but I knew what it entailed, and I hoped it would be enough.

So there I am, working as part of team Lennox, run by Pannix Promotions. I only came to look after Kevin Lueshing and he didn't even get a match in the end.

There were a lot of matches that weren't anything to do with Panix, so I could sit and watch. I was given a ticket in the second row, sat with Kevin to watch what fights I could.

One, to my delight, was my hero Julian 'The Hawk' Jackson, fighting some young fella called Gerald McClellan. I was confident in Julian, having lost only one fight in his long professional career. That was to the unbeaten Jamaican 'The Body Snatcher' Mike McCallum.

Right from the beginning Gerald was dominating the canvas, I was shocked when Julian was taken out in the 5th.

There were other times when I was on call to get the fighters out on time. They were always hyped up ready to go an all I had to do was open the door, generally they couldn't get out fast enough.

There was one exception. I politely knocked on the changing room of Lennox, one of his team came to the door and said he was still asleep. Who sleeps just before a fight?

Only Mr Lennox 'Ice Cool' Lewis, as he was known in Canada before he was transferred back to the UK, his birthplace. They soon got rid of that name, not really right for a World Heavyweight Champion.

Eventually they got him ready, and he casually walked to the ringside. I'd had a bet that he would win in the first five rounds. The first five rounds went and everybody was shocked at how he had showed no aggression at all. In fact the two black guys next to me said, "Your guy's a pussy!" I really had no reply to that, Kevin just looked at me, he was obviously equally as unimpressed. Tony Tucker just wasn't in the fight, an eventuality Lennox took him out. Summit he could have done in the first couple of rounds.

Lennox was, in those days, too lazy to even hold his hands up and his trainer little Pepe Correa was too scared to tell him. This proved to be his downfall when he fought underdog Oliver 'Raging Bull' McCall in Wembley.

I was looking after Oli for Don King at the time. DK had instructed me to take him to a 'Fatfarm' in Bedfordshire. What he meant was Henlow Grange Health Spa, a big country house, hosting guests on short term health treatments. They were all women whilst I was there.

The reason I had to take Oliver so far away from London was he had been taking crack on a regular basis in USA. They feared him scoring the gear whilst in the Wembley Hilton, where the rest of DK's team were.

In the last few days before the fight, Freddy Brown, trainer, and Greg Page, ex-World Champion, his sparring partner, appeared and half heartedly prepared him for his clash with Lewis. Nobody thought he had a chance, but everybody made out he had. On the last day, his Manager, Big Jimmy Andrews, appeared in good time to travel down with us in my 560SEL Mercedes to Wembley to join the rest of DK's men.

Leaving Henlow Grange we had to go through Bedford town. We were on a large roundabout in the town centre when I got lost, not sure which turning to take. We slowly travelled round it, whilst I looked for a sign to London. Behind us was a driver in a hurry, he started blasting his horn but I took no notice and continued driving slowly. Then this bright red Escort XR3i screamed round us and pulled up blocking our passage. We sat and watched in amazement as a twenty year old short stocky boy with a shaved head and gold earrings rushed towards us and knocked on my window.

Simultaneously both Greg Page in the back an I opened our tinted windows. His face was a picture as he looked in, open mouthed, at me, Oliver, Fat Freddy,

Greg Page all heavyweight boxers and twenty stone Andrews. This eight stone boy was looking in at a joint weight of over ninety stone of men. He left us even faster than he had arrived! That would make a great story in a Bedford pub that night.

On the way down to London, Freddy was giving last minute instructions to Oliver, telling him that every time Lewis dropped his guard, which we all knew was often, he was to throw any punches he could, using his strength to punish the Champ. In the ring first round, Oliver unleashed lots of punches, some strong but a lot doing nothing to upset the confident Lewis, whose hands seemed almost permanently by his side. Lewis was in one of his lazy moods and wasn't offering a lot in return.

The second started the same then Oliver give him a powerful straight right, putting him on his arse. After he got up, the ref waved him towards him and Lew nearly fell on him, as he stepped back it was clear to see from the front round, Lewis' knees were wobbling.

Second round TKO and there was now a new WBC World Heavyweight Champion, what an upset that was. I was stood beside cameraman Eric Guy, in the first round, when he said to me, would I stand behind the camera a minute, whilst he went to speak to someone. I obliged and was still there when Lewis went down. I was so shocked that I shouted out "Fuckin' 'Ell". Little did I know, but Eric had recently fitted a mic on his equipment. For weeks to come, the trade people that had bought his videos, would shout at me "Fuckin' 'Ell".

We all went back to the Wembley Hilton, now with Cutty in tow, DK's famous cuts man. Oliver went straight to the reception and made a phone call, screaming down the line that he had won. I was to find out later that he was talking to Mike Tyson who was in prison at the time.

The Sting 2001

Owning pubs in South London you see things you wouldn't see anywhere else.

This was a well organised sting in my car park at the front of my pub, The Belvedere in Peckham.

I was sitting by the window upstairs in my office, when I heard a crash out front. I looked out to see a £100 Nissan embedded in the side of a £40k Porsche. The skinny black man driving the Nissan was running off up the road. A big man got outa the Porsche and took chase. Meanwhile, another Nigerian looking man had appeared around the other corner, he went straight to the £40k car, pressed the catch to open the boot, pulled the keys out of the ignition and took the mobile phone from the centre console, I could see it all from upstairs. He then removed a large bag from the boot and ran off in the opposite direction to the other two.

This was a clever sting to relieve someone of a large bag of cash, I was to find out. Of course, I never saw a thing.

A couple of minutes later, the big man returned to the pub to find his boot open and the contents gone along with his keys and phone. No doubt the thieves numbers would have been stored on his mobile.

He couldn't even drive off, he was stuck in the pub, waiting for a locksmith he had called on the pub phone. He told me the story.

He wanted to buy some drugs to take North, where he was a local dealer. He had met some guy who could fix him up for the price of £35k. The meeting had been arranged in my car park. The driver of the Nissan had disappeared around the corner and it wasn't until he got back to his car, did he realise what had happened. A good days work for two Nigerians and a £100 Nissan!

Reg Kray's funeral

Things were never good between the East End and the Southside in London. The Kray twins were pissing off the families that ran the Southside. It was all to come to a head in 1966, in a Catford club called Mr Smith's, when Kray gang member Dickie Hart turned up there and got shot dead. This caused Ronnie to shoot dead the East End defector George Cornell the next day.

Mr Smith's was owned by a big multi club owner from the North called Dougie Flood. The only problem was, he didn't know how to handle the local villains that frequented the gaff. He was advised to ask Eddie Richardson and Mad Frank to look after the joint in exchange them having their fruit machines in there. It now was the daily haunt of the top South London chaps, no place for Eastenders!

Thirty five years later, the East End problems didn't exist any more. They still got a mention now and then, but they were both serving life sentences.

Eddie Richardson once famously summed them up as "A pair of brainless East End poofs. "

That opinion pretty well echoed around the Southside for many years.

Reggie was the last to die, it was in Norwich in 2000. As a sign of respect, it was decided by some Southside villains, to make up a posse of properly dressed chaps to travel across to Chingford, for that purpose.

It was an early service and what was meant to be an hour or so journey, turned out to take nearly three hours in the rush hour traffic. By the time we had arrived, the little church was already full. Kate Kray, Ronnie's ex wife, was very quick to turn us away and shut the church yard gate with no manners at all. We had come to show respect but there was none in return from this woman.

We waited respectfully outside in the street until the church emptied through the side gate into the cemetery, then we walked down to the big public gates in the street to find them locked. This was Kate Kray's way of running the show.

My good friend Stilks, or Stellakis Stylianou his real name, has wrote a story about the proceedings in his fantastic book [1].

Stilks takes it from here.

'We got to the cemetery in plenty a time and all the security had radio control with each other. We were told to be on our fucking guard and make sure that only the hearse and official limousines got in. It didn't matter who they were or how big the face was, they weren't allowed to be at the graveside. Those were the orders.

That's when we got a message that there quite a lot of people milling outside the gates of the cemetery and some were getting shirty with the Ol' Bill. I thought, fuckin' hell, don't tell me it's gonna go off here.

Some were shouting, "we've got a right to go in, it's a public cemetery," and all that bollocks.

Jacko (the security team captain), goes- "Right let's get down there and sort it."

"Sort who? Who's down there?" I asked.

"There's Charlie Breaker and his Mob, Big John Daniels and his mates and Courtney with his lot for starters." And I'm thinking, fuckin' hell, I know them.

"Jacko, I know them blokes," I said.

"Well you'd better come then."

"No I mean I know them. I can't fuckin' go down there and tell 'em they can't come in!"

"Well, it looks like your going to be the best fella for it. They aren't going to listen to anyone else are they?"

I thought, fuckin' hell but I went down there with Jacko and I could see Ol' Bill we're getting a bit worried. They thanked us for coming down there and asked if we could get some of the faces to move out of the way. They were all wearing dark Crombies with their dark glasses on an overcast day.

So I said to 'em, "look chaps, don't take it out on me or Jacko but the wishes of Reggie's wife are that it is close family and friends only."

"Let the cars in and let them do the small graveside service and if you want to show your respects when they come out and have gone, you lot can go in. What about that?"

One or two of them were murmuring about it not being fair, so I said, "Listen, it's a cold day, I'll tell you what I would do, I would go down the pub an' start celebrating from now until they've all gone and then come back and pay your respects. They all peered at each other through their dark glasses and then they must have decided I was fuckin' Einstein because most of them thought it was a brilliant idea and off they went down the pub.

But not Daniels, Breaker or Courtney, them and a few others took Jacko to one side to have a word with him.

That's when he said to me, "Look Stilks, do you think we can let this lot in by the other gate. They've promised they'll stay away from the cameras and the relatives and their respects quietly. They have been friends of twins for a long time, although his wife doesn't them in, do

127

you think we can get them up there with no trouble?"

"I don't see why not, as long as they stay out of the way," I said.

So we managed to get a few faces in and they were out of the way and no one noticed them. But they showed their respects, which I thought was a nice thing to do.'

Thanx me ol' mucker Stilks. A life time friend.

1 Stilks - The True Story of the Hardest Doorman in Britain ISBN 1903402956.

Earnie Shavers 2003

Joey Pyle was having an off week, he was getting more of these nowadays since he contracted motor neurone disease. Every week he would come to me or phone me and say, look after my Joe boy, he needs this or he needs that...

Slowly he was passing the legal side of things down to his son Joey junior. Very soon, the unlicensed boxing shows were to be run by Joe Jr and Ricky English. Joe Sr was now just the man sat up at the top table with Roy Shaw and me, and any guests of honour, whilst Joe boy and Ricky ran the show.

One day I got a call from Big Joe, as Joe Sr. was often referred as. He had Earnie Shavers, an American Boxer, coming to help with some fundraising. Earnie Shavers, a two-time world heavyweight championship challenger, is known for being one of the hardest punchers in boxing history. He had scored 68 knockout wins, including 23 first round KOs. Would I host a night at my venue, The Park? I immediately agreed, it was an honour for me to be having him there. I also agreed to put him up.

It was heavily advertised and when the day arrived, everybody who was anybody, poured through the doors. Every top villain from London was there, and a few from outside town as well. These top chaps sat up at the bar, and the ones off the street, having paid their tenner on the door, smothered them with drinks, shaking their germans and getting their pals to photograph them together, as if they were lifelong friends. These pictures, framed, would join the collection on their bedroom walls, to show to others.

"All these villains in the pictures are my best pals!", they lied!

Everyone knew the SP but just got on with it, after all, it was raising money to help get some poor little sick baby to some far off country, to get a cure for the cancer or whatever they suffered from, summit they couldn't get in the UK.

Liam Galvin would be there, with his film crew, taking deposits on the finished VHS, on the promise of it going in the post the following week.

We never did large charities, only local ones.

What with the door, the auction, the donations from the more successful, a percentage of the VHS money and a big chunk out a the Jack 'n' Jill, there was always several thousand to hand to the grateful father at the end of the night. Sometimes they even briefly brought the poor child for all to see, very often that boosted the kitty even more.

This particular night Ernie and I had done the auction, amongst the items for sale were some real class bits that Earnie had bought with him, including signed photos of him an Ali.

Stilks, of the book – 'Stilks: The True Story of the Hardest Bouncer in Britain' was there and spent thousands on this top memorabilia. Stilks was always a lovable and generous man. A very powerful man in all respects but a true gentleman, unless you was fool enough to want to upset him.

The auction over, I could now mingle with the crowd. I had summit to discuss with my old boss Charlie Richardson, so I joined him up at the jump. Whilst in conversation, I got a tap on the shoulder, I turned to face a giant of an old man. "You're barred, get out of here now, before I throw you out!"

I stared at him for a few seconds before I realised I was looking into the face of Big Joe. The doorman from the Bonn Bonne club in Brixton when I was a teenager and in my early twenties.

"Remember me boy?" He said holding his two clenched fists in front of him.

"Too right Joe, they're not german bands, they're size 14 shovels. I've felt them a few times."

Big Joe was the only one in Brixton who could control me, in the end he wouldn't even let me in the club. Every time he gave me a chance, I would end up having a tear up. You couldn't blame him.

"You was a right handful boy, a doorman's total nightmare." He said in his gravelly voice.

I was 56 years old now, and he was probably nearly 80, he still was a very well dressed but hard looking man. Liam picked up on what was going down, so he bought his camera over and we put on a little show for the tape.

We did many such charity nights for variety of causes, they were all good fun and Liam with the film crew bought out the potential actor in a person.

One such night was to raise funds for Wendy, the wife of a good pal who wasn't gonna be there this time. Tony Lambrianou had taken his beloved dogs out for some exercise before having an afternoon nap. He did it every day, Wendy would wake him after an hour with a cup a rosy. The week before, she had taken him his rosy lee as usual but was unable to wake him. He had died peacefully in his sleep. He was only 62 years old.

Tony had little money, he'd spent fifteen years in

prison and had gone straight since he had been out, so we decided to do a fundraising.

Wendy turned up, tears still running down her pretty little face, and it had the effect of all The Chaps pulling out fists full of notes and stuffing them into the kitty. It was a very successful night, the best ever, culminating in all Tony's pals saying a little summit over the mic. Liam then got us all outside for interviews where many of us, including Tony's brothers, told our own stories about Tony.

Whilst out on the veranda, a Mercedes pulled up and out jumped a massive black man. It was our old mate Cass Pennant, head of the ICF. He was running across the road carrying a book, it was a signed copy of a recent book he'd published. 'The 6-5-7 Crew', the story of The Portsmouth football fan club, written by Kev Courtney and Vic Sylvester. I had a pride of place photo in the centre page spread, even though football violence never interested me. That night is available on Amazon by Liam Galvin of Gangster Films.

Another good night was 'Biggs' Night Out', arranged by Joe, and a brilliant auction of Ronnie's genuine personal possessions by his son Mike Biggs. Bruce Reynolds and his son Nick were there. They had flown him back from Brazil when he got ill and couldn't afford the medical treatment to save his life. They had done that here, but had kept him locked up in the security wing in HMP Belmarsh since.

As Nicky Reynolds had explained, if a foreigner, even an illegal immigrant, gets in trouble in the UK, they are entitled to legal aid but as a returning Brit we are not! The only way to appeal against the thirty year sentence was in a Crown Court and here's the catch, no one is allowed to stand in front of a Judge without representation. So he was denied his right to appeal for a shorter sentence on compassionate grounds.

So it was decided to run these nights to pay for his representation. After Jack Straw had objected to his release on many occasions, he was finally released after serving another nine years of which much of it was in hospital. He was finally pushed out the nick on a wheelchair, unable to talk and messed up by a number of strokes. Our Brixton boy, Ronnie Biggs, died in North London aged 80 years old. RIP.

My pal Lou

What a Gr8 friend he was, I could tell a few stories, we both loved life and loved to travel, that's just what we did. His earthy laugh still rings in me crust. 3 years gone... LOU SZULC

My pal Lou was a one-off, born July 1959 of a Polish war refugee family, they worked hard to get up the ladder. He started The Aquarium as one of 6 partners and ending up as just him and Tony.

A devoted socialite, he was known everywhere we went. Not just in the clubs but also watching football in his local. He was always good fun to be with and seemed to love everybody. Definitely everybody loved him. We travelled abroad together many times, I could go on... He phoned me here over the Festive Season promising to come see me in Spain again in the Spring.

LOU SZULC you broke your promise, but I still loved you man.

The Slaughter part 1

In the '80s I obtained a slaughter to use when I was in the UK.

For those don't know what a slaughter is, think of Arthur Daley's warehouse in "Minder". It's a place to unload lorry loads of hooky gear. I would buy anything by the lorry load as long as I had room, and being as it was a big commercial garage, it was very rarely full. I bought anything worthwhile, be it electrical, plant, clothes, booze, toys, Christmas crackers etc., there was no exception.

Sometimes there were funny moments, close digs, dig in the graves, shaves or distribution problems, here's a couple.

These blags were very often on Crimewatch, Morning TV etc. Often they were inside jobs, which always made it easier on the tea leaf.

There was a chain of upmarket off-licences called Bottoms Up. One of their drivers came to me one day and asked if I would buy a load of booze, a mixture of wine and spirits. Of course I obliged, after I checked that it was good stock and bound for an offy. Yes, he said it's bound for Bottoms Up shops. I had spotted them dotted around Chelsea and such places but not in the South East, so I assumed they must be upmarket shops and therefore good stock.

The truck arrived and my team had to get it off fast, so he could get from there and be on schedule with his job. He was going down the South coast somewhere with his load and planned to have breakfast once he got out of London.

I took my boys for breakfast just round the corner from the slaughter, in "Egg an' Bacon Tony's" cafe. After breakfast we went back to sort out the wines from the spirits and list the bottles ready for distribution.

It didn't take long for me to realise that these weren't no ordinary lily the pinks what we could sell locally. These were, without doubt, not cheap drinks. There were a few expensive brandies and whiskies etc. but not stuff you'd be likely to see on the shelves behind the jump of a South London battle cruiser. There was some amazing old ports and a lot of the wines were vintage as well, not your average "booze blag"!

The wine bars of the day were always more upmarket and a place for local successful criminals to show off. One such place was Gossips, on the border of the ghetto and the upmarket West Dulwich Village, where the posh Dulwich girls would frequent to find "a bit a rough". I was known well by the Gov'nor there.

"Eric how's it going geezer?"

"Busy and you?"

"I need a little dicky bird in your shell like."

Eric was a college boy but he had enough of the local geezers in to be able to understand their lingo.

"Come round the side to me store room."

I got my thomas cook out and proceeded to read the list to the Guv'nor. I couldn't pronounce a lot of it and Eric enjoyed correcting me.

"Blimey! Where did that lot come from, Knightsbridge? It's definitely not local, so I got no worry there."

"You see, I have just had new wine lists printed and

the majority of that wine is not on my lists. I'll have them vintage ports and champagnes and a couple a cases of Chianti though."

"How much you offering?"

"Read the list out again."

I read the list out again and Eric put in what appeared to be some generous offers. Eric wasn't a generous person, so they were obviously worth more than what I had thought. Any way, I had a good start, I'd sold summit, now down to the hard work of selling the rest.

There was one particular thing that was of no interest to anybody at all. It was a semi sparkling Portuguese rosé not unlike Mateus Rosé, but the bottles were a sort of rustic, hand made looking, ceramic things. I was partial to a bit a Mateus Rosé at the local restaurant with a Lobster Thermidor, so I give it a go and took a shine to it.

Well it's OK to have one case of chordy booze, that was explainable but a dozen, no. So the rest was spread out across workers and friends.

One such worker was 'Old Ma', as my cleaner lady was known. Maureen Brennan was a salt of the earth, you couldn't find a more kinder, honest and loyal lady like her anywhere. Well, knowing that every Saturday afternoon she hosted a party of old dears in her gaff, drinking wine and watching the box, I dropped a case off and went to spend the afternoon in the pub over the frog and toad, the Gipsy Queen. Life was getting good for this young fart smella.

Whilst swallowing the first half of my fourth pint of Guinness, Ma arrived, putting her handbag fiercely round my lughole, causing me to lose grip of the glass and pouring the remaining Nigerian Lager all over meself, the glass breaking on the floor.

"Serves you right, how dare you show me up in front of my friends like that!" she shouted.

"Like what, I've only treated them to a free piss up, I've done no harm Ma."

"Don't tell me you didn't know that wine was stolen!"

"Of course I knew, I wouldn't have it otherwise."

"Yes but it's all over the TV, Nick Ross on Crimewatch said that 'the first batch had been stolen before any had reached the shops, so if you see one of these bottles, it was definitely stolen'!"

"Does it matter Ma, come let me buy you a drink."

"Stick yr drink, I walked out of my own home because my friends all laughed at me, how embarrassing!"

"Sorry Ma."

The Slaughter Part 2

My different hooky merchandise had been mentioned five times on Crimewatch, that I knew of, and sometimes they created stories. Here's another.

Sat in the office one day, The Paxton Hotel at the bottom of Gipsy Hill, having a quiet light ale when in came a couple of boys I knew from The Castle at Tooting.

" 'Ow's it goin Charlie boy?"

"Hunky-dory geez, what brings you over to my neck a the woods?"

"Looking for you of course, got plenty a dosh!"

These were a flashy pair of Herberts, blazers with cravats and blond tinted hair.

"Depends what yr selling."

I looked for a private clark gable and the three of us sat round it. The chaps up at the jump kept their distance, they knew the apple.

"What yr got?"

"Two tone, leather jackets but not shiny like."

"You mean suede?"

"Yes that's it I guess."

"Is says on the box that they were made in Checo somewhere."

"Czechoslovakia?"

They both nodded with agreement.

"How many you got?"

"Don't know, ain't counted them."

"Are all the boxes the same size jacket?"

"I think so mate."

"Right, count the boxes, check the sizes and bring me one unopened box. I'm here for the afternoon now. Where are they?"

"In the rental van that we hijacked coming out a Heathrow airport."

"Where's the van?"

"In a lockup, off Tooting Bec."

"Right, don't move the van yet, just get the box to me asap please."

I retired back to the jump to finish my pint a snakebite, Guinness an' Cider. Ging turned towards me and smiled.

"They sounded like hard work. The smaller of the two jus' sat wiv his north an' south open the whole time, did he say anyfing?"

"No, not a word. They can't help being at the back of the queue when God was giving out brains but the boys have some bottle, hijacking a van outside Heathrow airport. The place is crawling wiv filth."

"Or jus' 'kin stupid." said Ging.

I just smiled and got on with the afternoon's drinking.

An hour or two later the smaller fella came back in the pub and headed straight for me.

"Tony's outside waiting for you."

"He's got a tongue then!" Ging said.

I threw back the remainder of my drink in one.

"Hi Tony, where's the box?"

"In the boot geez."

"Right, follow me to the slaughter."

I entered the slaughter with the two young fellas, taking the box off them, and opened it. In the box was just five beautiful grey jackets, mostly suede with some leather and totally unique, I'd never seen anything like these before. He asked the price, well they were so cheap, he didn't even bid them.

"How many boxes Ton?"

"Forty eight, 'cos we got one an' you got one."

"How many's that?"

"How many is what?"

"Never mind. It's two hundred and forty an' I'll have the lot. How long will you be?"

"About an hour."

"When you come back, gently tap the horn and I'll back you in. Stay in the van an' my boys will have you empty in two minutes. Then get the van outside the area as fast as, but drive sensible."

There was one of my fellas in the slaughter making a space, while I drove round to the Gipsy Queen and got another. Then drove to my drum and picked up the spondoolies.

I hadn't been back long when I heard the horn. I turned the brand new Avis hire van around and they reversed it in, reminding them not to get out. With these pair a goons, it could easy get 'loud'!

My boys had the van emptied in record time and I let them out, paying them the pie & mash through the window.

I decided to retail as many as possible before bulking the rest out. This open box was 2XL, a bit on the tight side for my liking but I returned to the pub with it on.

Back at the pub, the jacket was catching the mince pies of the fellas as I walked in. I gave it to Ging who knew what he had to do, he was smart like that.

Back at the slaughter I got myself a 3XL, loosed the Rocky, and locked up for the day. Me and my youngest worker, Micky Oakes, went back to my place, from where Micky went and I got some Ruby Murrays. We settled down in front of the goggle box with the Indian and a flask of Weston's rough rider. What happened next you couldn't make up.

"Crimewatch is on tonight, isn't it Boss?"

"I don't know, I'll check it in the paper."

"Yes it says here, it's on BBC 1 in half hour's time, we can watch it and see what those terrible criminals are up to now".

I was perusing the local rag looking for bargains when Micky shouted.

"That Nick Ross has jus' appeared and he only got the same jacket as you Boss!"

I stared at the box in amazement.

"That's a coincidence, isn't it Boss?"

"Let's hope so."

Well we just stared at the box for the whole programme, and no mention of jackets.

As he said ... "Well that's it for another week, goodnight."

I sighed and fell back into my green leather chesterfield.

"Oh no, I nearly forgot the last thing. Do you like my beautiful jacket? Well there's none available in the shops 'cos someone stole them all except for this one sample. So watch out out for anyone wearing one and let us know on the usual number, goodnight."

Next day I went to the Walworth Rd and bulked out the lot to a wholesale fence, still making a nice few bob though.

The Slaughter Part 3

The slaughter had its funny moments too and some with a happy ending as well, here's one such story.

One cold day in November, my new Ford Transit was just leaving the slaughter with a consignment of 'Next' shirts to get the labels changed. I had thousands of them and they couldn't go on the market with the label. The new labels just said 'Brixton Brand'. Anyway, we're getting away from the story....

The doors were wide open for a moment, as the van was driving out. Purely by chance, a plod, Sgt. Smith, a friendly old cop, on the beat, was ambling past and got a view into the slaughter. He was South London and knew the apple.

Before we could shut the bobby moores, he made his way in.

"Morning Charlie boy, blimey, how many dustbin lids you got?"

"What ya mean Sergeant Smith?" I said, trying to look innocent.

"You have a lot a toys here!"

It only took a second for me to think of a covering story.

"We're collecting for Dr Bernardo's Kids Homes, haven't you heard?"

"That's very benevolent of you Charlie boy. Do you mind if I get involved?"

"Of course not, Sergeant Smith. That would be

great." What else could I say, 'They fell off the back of a lorry'?

"Whilst on my beat, I will go round all the stores and let them all know where you are, will you pick up if necessary?"

"Of course, thanks so much Sergeant, gotta go now, have to pick some toys up from Streatham. Bye!"

Once the doors were shut, the workers inside just burst out with laughter and I joined in until we all had tears running down our boats. We weren't gonna get any work done for a bit now, so I decided we'd have an early lunch. Only thing was, when Sgt. Smith appeared, and quite rightly so, Taffy drove off with the van load of dicky dirts. I stuck a note on the locked door but left the gates unlocked, so he could park the van on return.

'GONE TO THE GIPSY'

Wandering round to the rubba dub dub to get a 'pie an' a pint' for the boys, my mind was alive, working out a plan to cover my bottle.

By the time Taffy had arrived, I had it planned. I had to go down to Dr Bernardo's Homes ASAP and speak to someone, offering to collect for them.

After lunch, I got the boys to sort the boxes of toys out. All the boxes with pictures of toys on both sides stacked close to the doors and the rest stacked in the back, any pictures facing the other way. Meanwhile I had to go get a 'Collection Point' poster from Dr Bernardo's.

"Good morning, I have come to speak to the Head."

"OK, come in, its the first door on the left."

I walked up to the big oak bobby moore, there was a sign on it 'Headmaster'. It took me back to the five years I lived in a place like this. I knocked on the door.

"Enter!"

"Please Sir." I felt I was ten years old again.

"What can I do for you, young man?"

"Well you see Sir, I was bought up in a place like this and I wanted to put summit back into a local home. So me an' Sergeant Smith from Gipsy Hill Police station, planned on opening up a collection point."

"Fine, what do you intend to collect?"

"Toys for the kids' Christmas, Sir."

"Great. Well we have a Christmas Party every year on the Saturday before Xmas and we always invite our benefactors, so you and the Sergeant are welcome alongside any volunteers."

"There's some collection point posters on the table by the door."

"Thank you, Sir."

"No, thank you, kind Sir."

It felt strange being called Sir by a Master in a kids home.

I felt good in myself, in fact I felt warm on a cold winters day or was it just the Children's Home central heating system! I was gonna part with a small percentage of my profits for a good cause and the posters on the van and slaughter covered my bottle and glass when moving or storing toys of any description, of which there were many this time of the year.

It didn't take long for the Sergeant to persuade the local businesses to contribute some toys, even if they didn't sell them!

Even though no old bill was welcome really but I put up with the occasional visit to the slaughter by the Sergeant, who was even more impressed when he see the official posters. Hunky-dory.

Strange world

Sometimes, us old unknowledgeable folk think about things we learnt on our world travels. We will never know as much as those fifty years our younger, but we can try.

Bob Dylan once wrote…

"I was older then, I'm so much younger than that now."

Dylan's lyrics weren't always easy to decipher but this one seems easy to me. You start life thinking you know everything and when you mature you realise that you know nothing.

Anyway, I'm getting away from the subject.

Living in both Brixton and Jamaica, the Jamaican culture is one I understand very well.

Jamaica has, over the years, had the misfortune to lose many lives to tropical diseases. Probably the worst in my time was the Dengue fever, it wiped out practically whole towns and villages.

There is this image of the Rasta man 'passing the spliff to to left hand side', well I never ever experienced this in JA. In fact a true Jamaican in the UK won't share his spliff with anybody, if he likes you, he will give you summit and tell you to roll your own.

In my early years in JA there was no such thing as a Rizla. You could roll some ganja in a piece of brown paper, but more commonly in the bush, West Moreland and St. Bess, we smoked pure weed in a kutchie or chillum. It was shared, yes, but everyone had their own 'rag' or 'safi', which they wrapped around the mouthpiece of the pipe before putting their lips on it. These 'rags' were kept in their back pockets, 'Ragamuffin Style'.

Who remembers South London boxer Lloyd Honeyghan '86 World Welterweight, the 'Ragamuffin Warrior' with a white silk 'rag' sewed onto the back his black silk shorts?

Today, where we can't go into a supermarket without a mask, we feel there is no wrong in people getting together in their houses or clubs and sharing spliffs.

We can't dance together, I mean we might end up getting a peck on the lips, which is not considered safe. No kissing please!

Surely sharing a spliff is like kissing and they put their tongue in your mouth.

You never know, you might even take the flu home to your family this winter.

It's a strange world we live in.

Kelly's story 2001

Kelly Moore has been with Charlie Breaker for two years. Charlie, an ex-gangster, has served eight years in prison for crimes including GBH, ABH and malicious wounding. A former associate of the Richardson's, he has also acted as boxing promoter Don King's bodyguard. He is now retired.

Kelly says: "People imagine all kinds of things when you tell them you're living with an ex-villain. When we got together two years ago, my friends wondered if I was getting together with a maniac. At times, I did wonder myself. I'd meet his friends and they'd swap stories about him - how he was called Breaker because he broke bones, hearts and laws, how he'd had his face ripped apart in knuckleduster fights, beaten up prison guards and even pulled someone's teeth out with pliers. But with me, he was the perfect gent. When we met, my mum had just died, I was living in a horrible house, working as a barmaid, had hardly any money and a boyfriend who could be violent. Despite the stories I'd heard, I put my trust in Charlie and he's never let me down. We've never had a cross word. Every woman needs looking after and I knew I'd found a man who'd do that for me. He was Mr Right. He won't let anyone raise their voice to me. The children call him Breaker. To us he's a gentle giant".

"I now live in a country house with an acre of land at the front, six acres of woodland behind, stables, snooker room, bar, jacuzzi and a library. I don't see my old friends any more because this is my new life. I've never asked where the money came from - I don't want

to know about Charlie's past. I've only seen him fight once. Someone shouted at him while we were in the car one day: "You think you're hard, eh?" Charlie dragged the man out the car, punched him to the ground, picked him up, punched him down again and then threw him over the bonnet. I shouted for him to stop. I did wonder how far he was going to go. But when I told him to stop, he did."

"He hasn't had an easy life. He was brought up in council home school, approved schools, Borstals and did time in prison, but he has earned respect and has put the life of crime behind him". "I've never asked for anything from him. I only want to be part of his life. He buys me presents though and I have a ring which fits on two fingers, like a knuckleduster, with KEL spelt out in twenty seven diamonds. I tell him if he ever leaves me or upsets me, I'll imprint my name on his face with it."

Kelly Breaker

The Greatest

"I ain't draft dodging. I ain't burning no flag. I ain't running to Canada. I'm staying right here. You want to send me to jail? Fine, you go right ahead. I could be going to jail for four or five years, but I ain't going no 10,000 miles to help murder and kill other poor people."

"If I want to die, I'll die right here, right now, fightin' you. You are my enemy, not no Chinese, no Vietcong, no Japanese. You are my opposer when I want freedom. You are my opposer when I want justice. You are my opposer when I want equality. Want me to go somewhere and fight for you? You won't even stand up for me right here in America, for my rights and my religious beliefs. You won't even stand up for me right here at home. "

In 1966, Ali refused to be drafted into the military due to his religious beliefs and opposition to the Vietnam war and was found guilty of draft evasion and stripped of his boxing titles. He stayed out of prison whilst appealing to the Supreme Court where his conviction was finally overturned in 1971.

Only in America, nowhere else in the world would anybody be stripped of their boxing titles and not allowed to carry on their chosen sport because of their religion, or their beliefs. I missed conscription in the '60s, I was just too young, but I done three Borstals instead. There was not a lot a difference in my mind; military style parades, marching everywhere and kit inspections, spit an' polish boots, etc. I lost my chance to box for a good reason, I kneed a police cadet in the balls, whilst in the ring. Perhaps Ali should have kneed Lyndon B. Johnson in the cobblers as well.

Fuck you Uncle Sam!

Bish

Anyone who has lived in the Brixton area, especially the Jamaicans, if they didn't know Jimmy Bish, they knew of him. He had killed fifteen people it was said, mostly in the little Brixton shabeens. He had escaped conviction of all of these due to the fact that the Brixton community were stum. Mum was the word, you didn't even tell your Mum! The local cops found it hard to get evidence around here.

Here's an example. I had a lovely pub overlooking Norwood Park, it was all windows at the front, taking in all the trees and bushes of the park.

One day, an argument started in the bar, I was quick to get it out of the pub into the park. A massive fight started, two sets of people trying to hurt each other. It wasn't long before the cops arrived, unfortunately there were a couple of straight families living opposite, who obviously had informed them of the affray.

Dozens of cops turned up and quickly got it under control. Then, a top brass cop and about ten PCs turned to the pub.

"Charlie, we want to see the films from your camera." Said the cop wearing all the brass.

"Sorry to disappoint you Guv but it's only a bobby, there to make people think that they are being watched."

"Right I need you to lock the doors now, we need to talk to your punters." I cooperated.

The top man then took me in the back room.

"What's this fight all about?"

"Ain't got a scooby, Boss."

"You saying you didn't see anything or anyone you knew?"

"Yes Boss, I was in the cellar changing a keg."

He stood over me for half an hour whilst the customers were being interviewed by the other cops.

"Right, you stay here, I need to talk to my men."

He walked into the main part of the pub and consulted his officers, then returned to me.

"You must have massive toilets here!"

"What you saying Boss?"

"My men have interviewed fifty four of your customers and fifty two were in the carzy!"

That's the way it was amongst the working classes of the Brixton Manor. Right and all!

Back to Bish, as he was known, he was finally captured for summit, I didn't know what. Well, I was banged up in Brixton Prison, again. I was Cat. B. on the threes, which meant every time I went down the stairs to collect me bit a scram, I had to pass the cages. There were only two in HMP Brixton, and Bish was in one, surprise surprise!

"Oy CharlieB, come here!" he would shout as I passed, but the screws kept me moving on, nobody was allowed near the cages. Too dangerous!

I'd known Bish since we were young and we had always got on. He would take the piss if he could but he knew me better than that, in fact we could have a good old banter, more than most would dare.

A lot of the generation below me, mostly full or half blood Jamaicans were at the bar one day, we got on well, I knew more of their culture than they did! I had one well known family of half caste men around me a lot, the Huggins, good people.

One day, in walked Phil Huggins and Bish. All the youngsters at the bar would know who Bish was, without actually knowing him. I was brought up with him, different ball game.

As they walked through the door there was a gasp at the bar and lots a open mooeys. I decided to liven up their afternoon.

"Hey, what you doing in my pub, dirty n*****?"

"What ya saying honky boy?"

The boys at the bar gasped even more!

We walked slowly towards each other like a shoot out in a Western movie. He was getting the drama of it too. Then at the last moment, we lifted our fists and grasped each other's shoulders and kissed necks, a sign of respect where I come from.

There was even more wind being exhaled up at the jump.

I called for some drinks and we sat at a table.

"I jus' been up the Palace spar, we could run dat, me an' you, ya know."

"No!" I said "Wa' ya are mean man?"

"Jimmy, I already run it mate!"

He never mentioned it again and we had a fair sesh. Then Phil said it was time to go, he had to meet his brother Les and nephew Stephen down the road, so they both left after a few hugs. I had definitely scored a few brownie points with the younger crew that day.

An hour or so passed, and a punter came in talking about a stabbing down at the local Jamaican bakery. Well what's new, we did live in 'Murder Mile'.

I was later to get the full story. After Jimmy left my boozer, he got hungry and ordered a load of stuff from the bakery. He was a pound short to pay the bill. He turned to a Jamaican guy I knew as Slippery Steve, stood there with a baby mother and his pickney. He asked for a pound and Steve Parrish refused, Bish lost it and stabbed him sixteen times and he bled to death in front of his family before the ambulance arrived.

He served sixteen years.

Mr Nice

In the '80s during my peak period of supplying Brixton with their smoking requirements, I was buying weed that, unbeknown to me for many years, was then being brought into the country by a certain Howard Marks.

Joey was the main distributor to the London area, he supplied Jimmy who was responsible for South London, who in turn supplied me, Breaker, also known as Mr Brixton or on the Jamaican front line, CharlieB.

Howard, Joey and myself had all served prison sentences around that time, so it wasn't until the late '90s that Joey introduced me to a Mr Nice at a boxing show in West London.

We became instant friends and were meeting up every time Howard came to London. He didn't drive, so I would pick him up from Brixton tube station and take him back to my boozer, where we would finish the day. Sometimes he would he happy to sit and tell his stories to my enthralled customers but sometimes he would want to go out.

On one such occasion, I had heard there was a Jamaican singer in town, being presented with Premier Promotions and hosted by an old Jamaican friend, Val Cornell. It was to be in The Anchor Inn, now a predominantly Jamaican pub.

Recently Howard had acquired an interest in the Jamaican culture, it was all new to him. He was in Terra Haute prison with black Americans, but theirs was a completely different culture. So I thought I'd take him to the little Brixton venue and meet my community first hand.

I never left the house without a suit on but going out to a JA event called for a bling suit! Howard dressed the part he played in life, crumpled trousers and a jumper with holes!

We jumped into my burgundy Jag and we drove into town. On entering the front door, big Val spotted me, and as is the custom in these parts, I got bigged up.

"Big up to CharlieB, big man in narcotics ya know!" He shouted into the mic.

When Howard faced me and smiled, I was lost for words. He hadn't got a mention and his position in the narcotics world dwarfed me by a long chalk.

I had to do summit. So I walked Howard across to the raised stage and said to Val.

"This is Howard Marks, the biggest narcotics man ever in the United Kingdom."

Val looked down to the only scruffy man in the room but realised he had to say summit.

In a soft muffled voice he said into the mic.

"Big up to Mr Breaker fren'"

Howard enjoyed mingling with the locals, as always in any situation.

He said on the way home.

"I wanna go to Jamaica Charlie."

When we got back, we had a couple of bevies but the pub was shut by now.

He wanted to go upstairs to his room and roll a spliff, whilst on the bottom step, he spun round an asked if I had any food available.

"There might be some jerk chicken left, I'll look."

Sure enough there was a silver tray with an arrangement of Jamaican food cooked earlier by my

Jamaican nanny. I bunged a couple a bits of chicken on a plate and took it to his room.

He had taken his trousers off and was stood there in his boxer shorts. He pushed the little mattress to one side and proceeded to crumpled his strides up before laying them back under the mattress.

I roared with laughter, this was so funny.

"What's funny?" said the Welshman.

"When I was in institutions, I use to sleep on my strides to ensure jus' a crease on the front an a crease on the back. Your gonna have two hundred creases!"

He then saw the funny side of it. Back home where he came from, Mother done it for him.

When he started doing the 'Audience With' shows, I'd drive him where ever it was and we'd go to the dressing room to relax a while before he went on stage.

One time he was at the Hackney Odeon, now a live music venue with a massive stage.

Well I didn't do East End very often, but I knew that it was a lengthy drive during the day, taking up to three hours to get to certain parts. So I allowed lots of time for the journey. A couple of the chaps wanted to come with us.

"I've never had so many bodyguards!" Howard quipped.

We were looking a proper firm when we were met by Dave the owner. Apart from Howard, we were all suited and booted lumps. The boss took one look and said.

"I'll take you into my bar and you can have what you want, if I can be seen with you."

After being seated by our private waitress, we were asked what we wanted to drink.

I chirped up straight away.

"What champagne you got?

"Which one would you like?"

"Verve Clicquot, yellow label. OK boys?"

There were lots of smiles and nods.

"We're have two for starters!"

"You're a boy Charl!" said Howard.

"Here's a stone rich guy, who wants to be seen wiv us, let's milk it!"

With the waitress and the bubbles came the Boss, he was definitely making the most of it.

So was we!

With the second two Cliquots, I ordered five brandies to take the edge off the dryness of the bubbles. Howard was happier mixing it.

After the third order, Howard decided to go to his room. I sent the boys down into the audience to get some good seats, and I ordered number seven bottle to come with us. Once in the room, I produced this wrap of hash oil, the strongest smoke there was and passed it to the ganja guru himself, to try it. Howard rolled a big spliff, enough for four people but there was only him and me there, and I didn't smoke!

Needless to say, on top of the champs and brandy, it was taking effect. Howard's bottom lip dropped like I never seen before. He was out of it.

"What the fuck, that's good shit." He stuttered.

"Don't worry mate, I got some charlie in mi pocket."

A couple a lines later, he started swaying as we was told we were on.

He reached into his bag and pulled out a Russian fur hat and a bottle of Vodka. Why he wanted these I hadn't a clue.

I had to hold the back of his trousers on the way down the steep stairs, has was totally shitfaced.

Once back stage, he tried to pull himself together but he wasn't getting very far.

He managed to get to the chair before he collapsed into it.

He opened his mouth and the words that came out were unintelligible. The more he tried the more the audience applauded and cheered, thinking it was part of the show! He was off to a good start.

He took the Russian hat off an on a couple of times but I didn't see the relevance. As for the vodka, he needed no more. How we got back Southside that night was a miracle.

Mr Nice, the Film

Howard and I became good friends, and when I moved to Spain, he visited me there several times.

One day in 2009, I got a phone call from him. He had a friend coming out to Alicante, could he give him my number.

Of course I said, yes, and asked him what he would be needing, so I could get it ready for him. He told me, and I went out and got what was requested.

One day the phone went, a Welshman answered, so I assumed it was Howard.

It was his friend, he had the same South West Wales accent as Howard.

He said he was at The Meliá hotel in Alicante, and would I give my address to a taxi driver. I obliged.

Later I heard an argument going on outside my gates, it was the Welsh and a taxi driver arguing about the fare.

I rushed out to sort it. The Welshman was waving a 100€ in his hand an' the cab driver, in Spanish, was telling him it was only 70€. He thrust the 2 x 50€ in the car and we entered my garden.

We sat at my big table on the terrace and he discussed his requirements.

Then I asked what he was doing over, was he on holiday?

"I can't believe Howard didn't tell you!"

"Tell me what?"

"That we are filming some of Mr Nice in Alicante."

"Well I knew that the filming was in progress, but I didn't know it was in Alicante."

"I starts in three days time and Howard has said to the Director, Martin Rose, that he would like to have your family as paid extras. I discussed it with the casting director and he would like you to be there for the second day, you up for that?"

I looked around me and there was a lot of nodding going on. So I agreed.

He gave me the number of Alex Johnson, casting director.

"So what part do you play in it?" I asked the Welshman.

"Isn't it obvious? Mr Nice, of course!"

I felt divvy for not realising it, after all, he was Welsh and had long hair.

"I'm Rhys Ifans." He said.

"Are you a film star?" Asked one of the kids.

"No, I'm an actor."

That sent someone scampering off to the computer, who came back and replied.

"You are a film star!"

It turned out that he was in dozens, including starring in 'Kevin & Perry Go Large', 'Notting Hill' etc.

Then the attention was diverted to Rhys's needs.

I had already poured him a glass of cheap local wine, he was impressed!

"Good bit a wine that Boyo!"

"Well it is 90c a bottle!"

We all laughed.

Three days later, we were on our way to Alicante's Old Tobacco factory.

Here I had a living trailer for the family, next to the famous Arab comedian Omid Djalili, who played the part of Malik in the film.

The first day we all travelled to Alicante airport to

film Mr Nice entering the country, outside were parked a lot a '70s cars.

All my family were about to be filmed as extras, coming out of Arrivals. When the casting director came up to me, put a cap on my head, pulling it down to half cover my face.

"Try and keep your face covered, we have another part for you."

Later I was to find out that I was being cast as a London gangster in an American jail with a couple of talking parts.

The next day I dropped the family off and returned to continue filming in Alicante.

Over the next five days I was cast to do three small talking scenes.

During the first day Howard appeared to do a cameo part as the an owner of a Dutch coffee shop. After, I went for lunch with Howard and Rhys, we had a great time over a couple a bottles of wine an arranged to meet in Rhys' hotel on the last day to go have a session in town.

Having completed all our Spanish filming, on the fifth day we met in Rhys' room, as arranged, and purely by chance all three of us were wearing black shirts.

Rhys had just taken delivery of the script for a part of a wizard in a Harry Potter film. The casting staff from the Potter film were in the room with him when Howard and I walked in.

We entered the room and Howard introduced himself to them as Hairy Pothead. We were in stitches. Howard had a terrific sense of humour.

After we went to a restaurant that Rhys had found in the old town of Alicante. He was recognized by the Manageress straight away and we were ushered into a private suite.

The food and wine were fantastic. Out of the four of us, I was the only one non-Welshman. Joining us was a Welsh writer called Chris Sullivan.

Towards the end of the food, Rhys called the Manageress over an asked her if she had the big prawns he had on his last visit there. When she answered yes, he asked for a portion for me.

I asked if they were expensive and she said that they were just twenty five Euros. I said no but Rhys won.

Five massive prawns arrived, like none I had ever seen in Europe before. I enjoyed my expensive snack, feeling a bit guilty about eating prawns at five euros each. I was later to find out that they were in fact twenty five euros each! Rhys paid the bill of 1400€ and we left.

After we left there, we went on an Alicante small club crawl, being turned away by several, we were finally admitted to a cosy little place by the square.

Settled there with some top of the range wine, we got our gear out and spent all night enjoying ourselves, so to speak. By the time we left there, we was completely out of it.

We tried hailing several taxis but seeing the state of us, they sailed straight past. We were doomed to walk back to the Meliá hotel on the Marina.

On the way back, Chris Sullivan got a photo of us, he later printed in his book Rebel Rebel.

The next day I said my farewells and drove back home. What a crazy week.

White Yardie

As a youngster living in Brixton, I made a good friend of another local boy called Bobby Gregory. Bobby lived in the next street with his wife Angie and two daughters. He was a very brave guy and loved a challenge, he would take on any delivery no matter what the danger. When things got hot for me, Bobby would load up his rucksack, get on one of his fast motorbikes and beat the cops to it every time. There were many times they took chase but he would fool them by taking to pedestrian cuts that the cops couldn't get through in a car. As I was into distribution of weed over a large area by now, he was becoming a major asset to my little organisation. We both loved a line a charlie as well, so we were often socialising together and having a laugh, especially about the stupid cops that we had fooled between us.

We had many Jamaican connections, living in Brixton, but he was the first one to have the bottle to go to Jamaica and capitalise on it. It wasn't long before consignments of Jamaican ganja were arriving here in Brixton, and of course I was the obvious distributor he needed. Being away so often, his relationship with Angie became distant and eventually they split.

On one occasion he had so much money waiting for him that he went straight out and bought a brand new Ducati Street Scrambler. It was right up his street. It wasn't a pretty bike, or mega big, but this 350cc street machine suited his life.

One day he appeared in my yard with a pretty blonde

pillion, they got off and he proudly paraded his new love. She was a prize, the complete opposite to his Brixton missus. He had come to tell me that he was back to JA in the morning with his new richard and would keep in touch about business. We hugged and I didn't see him for a while, although the mules kept arriving with new supplies.

He was clever about how he treated the mules, mostly women. A Jamaican could come into the UK for six months only if a resident signed them in as their responsibility. Once they were in, nobody ever checked them, many being in the UK for decades. We had a Jamaican woman that had a UK residency, Sandra. I would give Sandra the details of them and their time of arrival. Bobby paid the flight and a promise of some money on arrival, and of course Sandra had a few bob as well. It wasn't a fortune to pay to get these cases of strong Jamaican ganja into the country. There was a massive demand for it amongst the Jamaican community. It was every woman's dream to go to England and get a job, as money was scarce back home for them. To have a flight paid for them, get paid and signed into the country, these women would queue up all day for the opportunity, so Bobby could take his pick. There were no scanners in the '70s.

One day Bobby appeared in the yard, he was excited, his life had taken a swing over there. His girlfriend was pregnant, he was starting his own sound system and he was buying a house overlooking the ocean on a deserted beach called Fort Charles. He just needed all the money he was owed and get his vinyls boxed up ready for export. We were all happy for him.

Things carried on great for him for the next few years, and everybody was getting a buck. His sound system, Don Pelico and the One Love, was doing well. He had moved into his house at Fort Charles, he now had another daughter, and to top it he soon had announced that she was pregnant again.

Bob had a way of just appearing in front of you, as if trying to catch you unawares. I was in the pub with a couple of the workers getting a bita scran, a pie an' a pint, as it was many times. In came Bobby.

"Oy, oy, saveloy, no hiding from me! I went to the yard an' Taffy said you was down here."

I rushed to hug him and welcomed him back.

"How's it going mi ol' mucker? Are you a dad again or what?"

"That's what I'm doing back."

"You lost me there Bobby!"

"I brought her back to make use of the National Health Service. The hospitals out there are a bit touch an' go and she's due any day."

We had a couple a jars and I dropped the boys back to the yard. Meanwhile, I took Bobby back to my house to take up some floorboards and give him his share of the profits. We shook hands and I never saw Bob again until the now three of them were on their way to Heathrow to fly back home.

"Say hello to Harry Gregory," he said. I just looked at this little pink bundle of flesh and smiled. Newborn babies all looked the same to me.

It was about this time that I was getting educated about exporting to Jamaica. Bobby was into imports and he was gonna get into exports.

The first time I sent a container of spare parts to Jamaica, it went to the north part of JA, near a place called Ocho Rios or Ochi to the locals. The yard there belonged to a Jamaican truck trader called Patrick, I had met him in John Brown's Erith yard 'Truck Busters'. He had allowed me to have my container delivered there, for which I was very thankful. I'd never been to JA before, it was all a bit of an experience for a 22 year old English boy. I wanted to go see Bobby but there was no phones where he was now, and all I knew then that it was in the south. So it wasn't until he came over the next time that he told me he had moved to another beach front house in Blackriver in St. Elizabeth. Here, there was electricity, water, shops and bars etc., that didn't exist in Fort Charles.

Now we had exchanged details, we could meet up when I was over. Which we did, in fact I started getting my containers brought to a yard local to Bobby.

I had become friends with this fella called 'Paddle'. All Jamaicans have a nickname, some very strange ones but they always had a story behind them. They wouldn't always tell you the truth though. Here's an example, I met a photographer on the Northside called 'Mackerel'. Well it didn't take a lot of imagination to see why, I never saw a man with a face so much like a fish in my life. So kidding him up, I asked why he was called Mackerel, and he said it was 'cos he ate a lot a fish. Show me a Jamaican that doesn't eat a lot a fish, Mr Fishface, I wanted to say!

Paddle's boss ran the local petrol station, and he also had a gas yard where you could take your empty butane bottle to get it filled up. It was a very secure pound and made the perfect place to park my containers.

I would go an eat at Bobby's house and we would go out to the little bars after to have fun. As the kids grew up, I started to take them out for day trips to resort areas. Harry Gregory is now the famous comedian

White Yardie. Even as a very busy young man now he has taken time off to talk to this old man!

Jamaica

Every time I returned to Jamaica, the first stop was the Safari bar, a little bar that was all outside except the barman and the drinks.

I would get my driver to take me straight from the airport, and on arrival there, I would be updated with the local news. There was always summit that had happened.

On arrival to the bar one time, as I sat with my first Jamaican Guinness, a tale was relayed to me.

"Ya nor Big Andrew?"

"Big big n***** Andrew?"

Sure I did, every one knew him. He was the largest person in this little town. He was almost seven foot and about thirty stone. He could be seen walking back from the sugarcane fields, his massive hands hanging beside his knees, holding his machete.

Well, in Jamaica, because of the lack of money available for a young girl, they had 'envelope men'. They left their children with their Mother or Aunty and entertained men in return for an envelope on the weekend. This generally started anytime after they were about thirteen. It wasn't seen as prostitution.

On the outskirts of town, where everyone lived in wooden huts, lived Aunt Daisy and her pretty but very small sixteen year old niece Winsome. She had a visit every Friday, after he had been paid, by Big Andrew.

The arrangement was, Aunt Daisy would go up the road to spend an hour with her sister, returning later to collect her share of the wonga.

Well this particular Friday, Aunt Daisy left her sister to return to her home. On arrival, she could hear her niece still moaning, this wasn't normal, so she went back to her sister, who suggested that to last this long he must have got some Viagra, so they left it another hour.

On return, with her ear close to the door, she could vaguely hear the weak wimpers of Winsome.

"Help, help!"

She threw open the door to see that Big Andrew had expired on top of his little bit a pussy. Because of his size, she suspected a heart attack.

She rushed to the girls assistance but Andrew was too much for this little old lady, so she went and got her sister. They both failed to move this giant, so they called some young geezers off the street.

They managed to roll him over but the poor screaming girl was still impaled on his enormous penis and rigor mortis had kept it hard.

The boys then slid her off and she rushed into her Aunt's awaiting arms, still naked. The fellas left respectfully.

If there was ever a young girl needed a bit a counselling, it was Winsome.

Winsome was a pretty little thing but, most of the big money men preferred the 'Big Botty Gal dem'. As it sounds, these girls had some serious butts. Well eventually the 'gal dem in a bush', country girls had worked out a way of expanding their 'bottys'. A lot of people living in the bush kept chickens, or fowl as they call them. Caponising pills had just reached Jamaica. For those that don't know, caponising pills where injected under the skin of a young cockerel and it would castrate them and turn them into eunuchs. Once they had taken effect, the body turned the excess energy into more meat, thus making a lot bigger fowl to sell. So the gals dem tried it an it worked on their butts big time! These country gals were sporting butts the size of a small third world country! The more the men got excited, the more the gal dem took 'De Fowl Pill'!

Another amazing story I was told was the death of Aunt Lou.

Aunt Lou was a frail little old lady who fished from the riverbank on the estuary of the Black River. It was called Black River because the mangrove swamps on the edge of the river dyed the water black.

This river and its mangrove swamps are notorious for crocodiles, or alligators, as the locals called them and massive mosquitoes.

Aunt Lou only stayed long enough each day to catch two fish, one for her and one for her sister. She then went home, until one day...

Seen from the local 'Bonies Bar', those sat outside witnessed a giant croc jump up out of the river and take Aunt Lou by the head and disappear upriver.

One of the men ran to get a shotgun and boarded the boat with others, waiting to take chase.

About twenty minutes upstream they found the monster floating in shallow water. He was killed very quickly, as crocs can't just sink on wish, they have to wait for their body to adjust.

A rope was attached to the dead villain and he was towed back to the estuary.

The big male was rolled over onto his back and his belly carefully sliced open to reveal Aunt Lou. She was still intact but was no more alive. Crocs swallow their prey whole, so the hunters were hoping she might be still alive.

The croc was dragged to a quayside warehouse to keep the sun off it. It wasn't long before the locals were charging Jamaican press to see it and take photos. They got even richer when the press arrived from the USA.

Within a couple of days it had been skinned and chopped into shares for all involved. It measured at fifteen feet and eight inches, not the biggest ever but the biggest in Jamaica, a lot bigger than the average large male at eleven/twelve feet.

I wondered if I might get offered a crocodile skin belt in the near future!

Business in Jamaica

Waking up for the first time in Jamaica, the first thing you know is you're warm, then you're thirsty, that's dangerous and when you look out of the window, you realise how horny these native girls, uncorrupted by the UK, actually are. They don't know what a KFC is, what a fruit machine is, they don't have a TV, they have to make their own clothes. Shoes are expensive so many go barefoot, especially out of town in a bush. They are hungry. Last night when I arrived, I ignored the advances but things could change. Business always came first. Always! But fun comes second!

When I made it down to the yard, Patrick already had a punter waiting for me. Patrick told me that this guy wanted a starter motor for an Austin Cambridge and how much to charge. I unlocked my spare parts 'safe', my container, and found a starter motor for him. I took his dollars off him but wanted to chat a bit. When I asked about his job, the tall Jamaican replied that he had a top job, he was a carpenter and pointed to the pencil stuck in his Afro hair. He also said that this starter motor was almost the equivalent to two months wages. Shit I thought, I couldn't buy 2 pints with it in London. I had struck it rich. My spares were worth fortunes but the price of living was nothing in comparison.

Life was good here, but it was too much of a tourist town for me, the street hustlers were starting to piss me off.

So I went to meet my old mate Bobby Gregory

down south. The Brixton boy had landed in the south, St Elizabeth. Blackriver, where he was, had a got itself a name for crocodiles and mosquitoes but nothing bothered me.

I needed to empty this container and get back for the next. Bob told me about a friend with a spares shop in West Moreland. The Jamaican had recently moved back from the UK. He hadn't been open long and never had a lot a stock. I decided to make this little shop my first franchise. It was a start.

The franchise thing interested me, it meant I could earn without actually being there. Slowly, with every container came more franchises. Chicken George at Spanish town was one of the best shops. Then came Big Bill from the cold town of Mandeville. He had a big trade with the churchs etc. who wanted Transit parts. This was the new thing, taking orders.

One day I was introduced to a lovely man called Laughing Dave. He lived between Mandeville and Maypen in the days before the Maypen ring road. He had a proper brick built bungalow just off the main road.

Whatever you said, Dave laughed. He was a local wheeler dealer who was buying up all the old Austin J2s, chapel buses, as the minibuses were called. The BMC 1500 engines were tiring from dragging all the big Jamaican women up the midlands hills and were starting to squirt oil in protest. The ideal replacement was the Ford 2.0l V4 and it's floor change four speed box. Dave had it sorted once he met me. He was now getting regular supplies delivered to his address, fresh from the UK.

Back in London, the boys working the streets with their little breakdowns were flooding my yard with any Transit they could find. Ray the crane was ripping out the lump, the prop, axles and little more. Mark was busy running loads of shells to Henry Dixie's at Mitcham common. Everybody was happy, including Laughing Dave.

Meanwhile, I was busy touring the island looking for new franchises. Lots of Jamaicans realised that there was good money to be earned selling second hand parts but few had a good source. It would initially be cash up front only, but I started doing credit to those that realised where their bread was buttered. The more stock they had, the more money they could make.

One small problem was getting paid in Jamaican Dollars. These scruffy little notes were not recognised outside Jamaica. Life was so cheap there that it was only possible to spend so much. They were starting to build up in the container where I kept them. There was nowhere safer, that was for sure.

One day, spending some time with a local record producer Dennis Cole, he discussed this problem. Dennis recommended a local hustler called Dollar. This guy would buy £'s an $'s at above market rate from the tourists and stick his bit on before selling on to whoever needed them, mostly big time weed dealers, who wanted to get their ill gotten gains into the UK or the USA. I was up for this as well. Also, Dennis advised me about my own personal protection, as I was getting more money, people would be noticing, so I should always walk with a man and a gun. It wasn't a big price to pay, here money was hard but even harder to keep!

I started to go down South at the weekend, to spend time with Bobby. We would be all round the bars Friday night, life was good. Having the dollar we were very popular. It was usually daylight by the time we rolled in on the Saturday morning.

Saturday was always different, turtle egg punch was the speciality in the local fisherman's bar in the morning, and turtle soup would be on the menu that night. Turtle meat was bright green and didn't look very appealing to the foreigner, or *furriner* as we were referred to as.

The Green Turtle as it was known, just because of the colour of its flesh, was in fact brown and was in great abundance in the Caribbean, and had been considered part of the staple diet for many years. In the neighbouring island of Cayman, they have a turtle farm. They breed them from the eggs their turtles laid, and because they're in captivity they have over a 90% survival rate as opposed to less than 1% in the wild. The yanks that run everything on the islands close to USA weren't too sure about this farming to feed local people, and put pressure on them to release 10% back into the sea, to which they agreed. Now there are ten times more turtles there than there ever was! So a lot more are being caught in fisherman's nets in the South Caribbean Sea. More food for Jamaica and Cuba, they're not complaining, times are hard there.

Tens of thousands died from starvation and the lack of medical care after the abolition of slavery. Now with the 1962 Declaration of Independence, there was no more support from the British government, they were phasing it out but it had practically disappeared now. Times were getting hard again. The value of the Jamaican Dollar was declining, not good news to importers, finding they were getting less £'s to the J$ on the exchange. It wasn't a problem to me, yet.

Jamaican cops

The Babylon, as Jamaican people call them, have no wish to arrest a white man, it's far too complicated. White people had run the island for 100s of years and still had a certain power.

But on sight of a white man, the police had $ signs in their eyes, as did a lot of poor Jamaican people. The cops here weren't paid a lot, so needed to top up their wages.

There were always two options to sorting out any offence committed.

With Black Jamaicans, their policy was to shoot first and ask questions after. As we all know, there is a black clock, it always hours behind the conventional one!

I had foolishly told the actual flight arrivals time to my driver, which meant waiting over an hour in the Caribbean sun outside the new Montego Bay airport for my car to arrive. Meanwhile, I was being hassled by small time weed dealers.

"Ya wan ses?"

One dealer made the mistake of asking me twice. After an hour waiting in the sun, it was a big mistake.

"Yr mus need sum top ses!"

"Pass me dat!" I said.

He passed me the brown paper bag, I took a quick sniff and looked in it.

"Why you offering me this cheap mountain bush weed as sinsemilla? Only 20 miles away you are in West Moreland, the home of the best sensi in JA."

I threw the bag on the floor and screwed it into the road with my boot.

"Now get fuck away from me, pussyhole!"

A bit cruel perhaps but I didn't get hassled again, that's for sure.

Soon after my car arrived with Dan and two of the boys. It was a big V8 Vauxhall with blacked out back windows, so I got in the back.

The boys were drinking Guinness and smoking spliffs, they passed me a bottle. The return party had started already!

The co-pilot had his feet up on the dash, window open with his hand hanging out holding a spliff. He was taking a swig on his Guinness when they passed a Police Landcruiser. The cop immediately took pursuit after us with flashing lights and siren on.

Dan, my driver, decided to put his toe down, whilst one of the boys was explaining that a new law had just came out, forbidding drinking in cars.

The cops started shooting at us, as we drew away from them. I could hear the bullets pinging off the bodywork, I slid down the seat so that my head was below the window sill, the next might go through my head. Then, in front of us, was a big slow truck chugging its way up the hill. Dan decided to overtake the truck on a blind bend halfway up the hill, my heart was in my mouth. We had lost the Babylon and I just wanted to get off the road and chill in a bar somewhere. The boys wanted to make it back to Blackriver first but it was my turn to put my foot down. We pulled off the main road onto a little track and soon found a bar.

"A 'Q', a whites honeypot and whatever the boys want" I needed a stiff rum!

I turned to Danny.

"Why?"

"Why what boss?"

"Was it not better to pull over rather than risk our lives?"

"But Boss, I was saving you money!" He explained.

"I can assure you, I'd rather pay every penny I have on me than risk my life overtaking that truck on a road mostly used by big trucks."

This really showed me how cheap life was here in Jamaica.

We drank up and took a cross country route back home.

Because I had several outlets here in different parts of the island, I travelled a lot getting paid and picking up new orders. This time I had been to Port Antonio to look at a front row beach house for sale, it was very cheap. But like most very cheap things there's a reason, as was the case here.

I headed back home on the coastal road by Buff bay. I soon made it through St Mary into St Anne, and avoiding Ochi made my way to Faith's Pen. Here was the best takeaway in JA. I sat and enjoyed a 'Mannish Water' and got a 'Curried Goat' to go.

Further down the road, I crossed Linstead tin bridge and down to Spanish town. I had a franchise here, but I didn't need to visit it at the moment, so I headed back through St Catherine's. By the time I got to Old Harbour, I was falling asleep at the wheel, so I decided to book in at a little fuck hotel I'd heard of called The Hibiscus. I took directions and soon found it just out of own.

After putting my bits in the room, I went back down nto the hotel and ordered a Guinness, but no, they didn't sell drinks. So I thought I would go back down into town, where I knew a little bar.

When I walked in, there was an old pal of mine, Vic, sitting there drinking Vodka, unusual drink for a Jamaican. It was instant party time. The Q's were flowing and I was getting pissed big time.

Well, the time came that I was reaching tilt and I hugged everyone and left to go back to the hotel. Outside in the air, I fell apart, I was completely pissed.

I took the completely wrong route an ended up driving over rough land until I knocked the exhaust off. My drunken determination made me attempt to find the road again, and I got a puncture. Now I decided to sleep it off. Locking myself in, I slept on the steering wheel. I don't know how long I was there when I awoke, someone was knocking on my window.

"Hopen hup, it's the Poleece!"

I opened up and fell on my face, kissing the gravel!

"Sir, I must warn you, hin dis country it's against the law to drive whilst ya drunk."

"Yes Boss." Was the best I could manage.

"Dare two way we can do dis. You can cum back a Poleece yard an' chat wid me Sargent in de morning, or we sort it now."

I agreed now was great for me.

"You can pay us now."

I then realised there was two big officers and a young policeman.

I had my money in my pocket but was starting to get a plan together.

"My dollars are in the hotel."

He said I should get in the police car and they would take me there. But I said no way was I gonna leave my car here.

You have a puncture he said, to which I replied there's a spare in the boot.

"Junior, fit de man tyre dem!"

The youngster soon had the wheel changed and the big man said now we can go.

I said we couldn't drive it with the exhaust hanging off.

"How we can do dat?"

"I have some shirts in the boot on hangers, use one of the hangers."

"Junior."

"Yes boss I got it."

Within ten minutes the exhaust was fitted and we was on the way to the hotel, me in the police car.

Once there, I ran up the stairs to get my money out and put it on the cabinet.

The cop was banging on my door, I opened it and passed him J$1000. As I went to shut it he put his foot in the door.

"Dem tree of us yanow!"

I went back and got another J$2000 and passed it him. He was happy.

I went to bed and got me a good kip.

I woke in the morning and was trying to remember it all. I looked out the window to see my car, all four tyres were up, like the exhaust.

There was about J$65 to the pound at the time, so for £45, I had a tyre changed, exhaust repaired, a lift to the Hotel and got off a drink driving charge.

Result!

Glossary

Apple (core) - Score, as in understand, also £20
'Arf inching - Pinching
Aris - Aristotle
Aristotle - Bottle
Barnet (Fair) - Hair
Beak - Magistrate
Bees an' Honey - Money
Bird - Time in prison etc.
Bish bash (bosh) - Wash
Blagging - Stealing
Bluie - Lead
Bo-Peep - Sleep
Boat (race) - Face
Bobby (Moore) - Door
Bottle (an' Glass) - Arse
Bristol (Ritz) - Tits
Brown Bread - Dead
Bubble (Bath) - Laugh
Bubble (an' squeak) - Greek
Bugle - Nose
Butcher's (hook) - Look
Bwoy - Patois for boy
Captain Cook - Look
Carzy - Toilet
Chalk Farm - Arm
Chavies - Rommany for boys
Cherry Hog - Dog
Chiv - Knife
Choring - Stealing

Claret - Blood
Clark (Gable) - Table
Coney - Rommany for rabbit
Cred - Reputation on the street
Crust (a bread) - Head
Currant Bun - Sun
Dabs - Finger prints
Daddies - The top dogs on a prison wing
Daisy (roots) - Boots
Dancing bears - Stairs
Dicky (dirt) - Shirt
Dipped - Pockets robbed
Dipper - Pickpocket
Dog 'n' Bone - Phone
Dolly Dimple – Simple, as in a person
Drum - Home
Drummer - Small time burglar
Drumming - Robbing from a house
Dustbin (Lid) - Kid
Farmer's Daughter - Water or a quarter (ounce of hash)
Filth - Police
Flim - £5 note
Folding (matter) - Pound notes
Four by Two - A Jew
Fred Astaire - Chair
Frog (an' toad) - Road
Gavver - Rommany for policeman
Gazunda -Potty (that 'goes under' the bed)
Geezer - Man
Germans/German bands - Hands
Ginger (beer) - Queer
Glaswegian Kiss - Head butt
Golden Handshake - Payment/bribe
Gregory (Peck) - Neck
Gunga Din - Bin

Hank (Marvin) - Starving
Harry Dash – Flash, as in a person
Hinges - Ankles or feet
Holy Ghost - Toast
Hooray Henries - Upperclass men
Jack 'n' Jill - Hill, till or pill
Jam Jar - Car
Jimmy (Riddle) - Piddle or a fiddle
Joanna - Piano
Keeping Dog - Keeping watchout,
Knobbly (Knees) - Cheese
Lemon (curd) - Turd
Lily (the pink) - Drink
Liquid Cosh - Barbiturate injected into a problem prisoner to keep him quiet!
Lucky Dipper - Stripper
Lugoles - Ears
Manor - A London area
Mars Bar - Scar
Mince (pie) - Eye
Mitts - Hands
Moody - Fake
Mooey - Mouth
Moult - Rommany for a woman
Nanny Goat - Throat
Nelson (Eddies) - Readies, cash
Nick - Police station
North (n South) - Mouth
Oily Rag – Fag, as in cigarette
'Oysting - Shop lifting
Paraffin (lamp) - Tramp
Peado - Paedophile
Peckham (Rye) - Tie
Pen 'n' ink - Stink
Peter - Cell or safe

Pie 'n' Mash - Cash

Pigs Ear - Beer

Probo - Probation

Richard (the 3rd) – Bird, as in girl

Rifle (range) - Loose change

Rocking (horse) - Sauce

Rosie (Lee) - Tea

Rough (Rider) - Cider

Row - Fight

Rubba (dub dub) - Pub

Salt - Woman

Saucepan (Lid) - Kid

Scoobies - Amphetamine tablets

Scooby (doo) - (hasn't got a) clue

Scram - Food

Scratcher - Bed (scratch ya head)

Shuve - Counter/bar

Skin 'n' Blister - Sister

Sky (rocket) - Pocket

Sloane Rangers - Posh people from Sloane Square

Smoover - Overcoat

Sob/Sov - Pound (sovereign)

Spar - Patois for friend

Straight (runner) - Honest person

Sweaty (sock) - Jock

Swede - Head

Swede Basher - Country boy

Taffy (Apple) - Welshman

Tea leaf - Thief

Thomas Cook It - Book it

Titfa (tat) - Hat

Togs - Clothes

Tom 'n' Dick - Sick

Tom (foolery) - Jewelry

Tool - Foolish person

Totters - Rag 'n' bone man
Treacle (tart) - Sexy girl
Trouble/Trouble 'n' strife - Wife
Turd Burglars - Gay men
Twelves - Keys
Two 'n' Eight – State, as in mess
Uncle Fred - Bread
Whistle (an' flute) - Suit
Wid - With
Pie 'n' Mash - Cash

Printed in Great Britain
by Amazon